Readers Praise *Let's Play Math*

A creative and inspiring challenge to the way maths is usually taught ... packed full of ideas and resources ... In a culture where maths anxiety is now a diagnosable problem, this book shows the way to maths joy.

—J. McAndrews, Amazon.co.uk reviewer

With this approach I can teach my kids to think like mathematicians without worrying about leaving gaps ... I can't wait to take my children by the hand and head off to explore the wonderful world of maths.

—Lucinda Leo, NavigatingByJoy.com

I love math, but had forgotten why I developed a love for math in the first place. This book made me realize how experiences in my childhood lit a spark in me ... [and] shows us how we can ignite this fire in our own children.

—Carrie, Amazon.com reviewer

Great ideas and very well researched information.

—Cynthia McCarthy, Amazon.com.au reviewer

This book will change the way you look at math forever ... *Let's Play Math* challenges parents to teach their kids to 'think like mathematicians' and use their problem solving skills to really understand concepts rather than just memorize processes ... definitely a must-read e-book for all home-schoolers!

—Lilac, LearnersInBloom.blogspot.com

I loved how this book reframes our concepts of Math to recover an intuitive, living sense of numbers and the real world. ... Along the way, readers will learn games and kinds of behavior they can adopt to develop a Math sense in their children.

—Rafael Falcón, Amazon.com reviewer

Let's Play Math

How Families Can
Learn Math Together
—and Enjoy It

Let's Play Math

How Families Can Learn Math Together —and Enjoy It

Denise Gaskins

Foreword by Keith Devlin

TABLETOP ACADEMY PRESS

Tabletop Academy Press, Blue Mound, IL, USA.

ISBN: 978-1-892083-20-3
Library of Congress Control Number: 2016901133

Credits:

A few sections of this book were originally published in 1998 and 2000 as *Aha! How to Teach Math So Kids Get It,* and others originally appeared on the Let's Play Math blog.

Cover photo by Monkey Business Images via Shutterstock.

"McLemore Hotel," image courtesy of the Boston Public Library via Flickr. (CC BY 2.0)
https://www.flickr.com/photos/boston_public_library/6775629674

"Let the children play," extended quotation from Christopher Danielson, first published on Talking Math with Your Kids blog, August 31, 2015. Used with permission.
http://talkingmathwithkids.com/2015/08/31/let-the-children-play

"Fractal Terrain," "Kugleramme," "Al-Khwārizmī's al-jabr," and "Children learning maths" from Wikimedia Commons, public domain.
https://commons.wikimedia.org

"Dimension Levels" by NerdBoy1392 via Wikimedia Commons. (CC BY-SA 3.0)
https://commons.wikimedia.org/wiki/File:Dimension_levels.svg

"The Purpose of Word Problems," extended quotation from two articles by Andre Toom, Ph.D. Used with permission.
http://toomandre.com/my-articles/engeduc/index.htm

"Mathematistan: The Landscape of Mathematics," by Martin Kuppe, aka Zogg from Betelgeuse. Used with permission: "It's a Galactic Commons license; you can use it if you don't claim it's made by one of your species."
https://youtu.be/XqpvBaiJRHo

The best way to learn mathematics is to follow the road
which the human race originally followed:
  Do things,
  make things,
  notice things,
  arrange things,
and only then—reason about things.

Above all, do not try to hurry.
Mathematics, as you can see, does not advance rapidly.

The important thing is to be sure
that you know what you are talking about:
to have a clear picture in your mind.
Keep turning things over in your mind
until you have a vivid realization of each idea.

When we find ourselves unable to reason
(as one often does when presented with, say, a problem in algebra)
it is because our imagination is not touched.
One can begin to reason only when a clear picture
has been formed in the imagination.

Bad teaching is teaching which presents an endless procession
of meaningless signs, words, and rules,
and fails to arouse the imagination.

— W. W. SAWYER

Contents

Foreword

AUTHORS AND PUBLISHERS OF NEW mathematics and math education books frequently ask me to write a foreword or a cover endorsement. Denise Gaskins's *Let's Play Math: How Families Can Learn Math Together and Enjoy It* is not one of those cases. I volunteered to write a foreword. I did so because I wanted to help in any way I could to get this book into the hands of as many parents and math educators as possible, particularly the hands of the large number of homeschooling parents in the USA— many of whom purchase some of my books or listen regularly to my Math Guy segments on NPR, and some of whom email me and attend public talks I give around the country.

For, in the publishing world, the odds are stacked against Ms. Gaskins. She is not a professor at a major university, nor indeed any institute of higher education. Nor is she an "award winning career teacher." On top of which, she does not have a major publisher behind her. I could have put a "yet" in that last sentence, but I'm not at all sure her future success with this book will play out that way, though in terms of sheer quality it could if she wanted.

"So who is she?" you may ask. On the Amazon page for the first edition of this book, which she self-published under the banner Tabletop Academy Press, she describes herself this way:

> *Denise Gaskins is a veteran homeschooling mother of five who has taught or tutored at every level from preschool to undergraduate physics. She loves math, and she delights in sharing that love with young people.*

Here is how she summarized her mathematics education activities when I asked her for a bit more detail:

1978-1984: assorted jobs including volunteer tutoring, physics T.A., and a one-semester stint as a 6th-grade teacher in a private school

1982 (I think): B.S. in physics & science writing, Purdue University

1984-PRESENT: homeschooling mother of five

1992: began writing sporadically about math education

1995-2014: led math circles or math classes for local homeschoolers

1998: published my first booklets to accompany math workshops for homeschool groups

1998-2001: published bimonthly *Mathematical Adventures* newsletter for homeschoolers

2006: started Let's Play Math blog, originally aimed at homeschooling parents but the audience has widened over the years

2009: started Math Teachers at Play blog carnival to support creative math education in families and classrooms

2012: published *Let's Play Math* ebook first edition

2015: contributing author to Sue VanHattum's *Playing with Math: Stories from Math Circles, Homeschoolers, and Passionate Teachers*

2015: published two *Math You Can Play* books of number games (*Counting & Number Bonds* and *Addition & Subtraction*) in ebook and paperback

I deliberately left in the caveat in her 1982 entry as I find it particularly revealing. The physics major and the science writing, at one of the nation's top engineering universities, explain a lot about her success; the year is irrelevant, implying (at least to me) that she is not particularly interested in the university credential. Credentials play an important role in society, but they definitely get in the way of good education.

Denise and I have never met, but having followed her blog Let's Play Math for over eight years, I feel I know her. I first encountered her back in 2008, when I wrote a series of articles in my online Devlin's Angle column for the Mathematical Association of America, asking teachers to stop teaching multiplication as repeated addition.

Why did I suggest that? Because it isn't. See my MAA posts for June, July-August, and September of 2008 for explanations of why it isn't and why it is harmful to teach it as such, and then January 2011 for a brief summary of what multiplication is.[†]

---

† *https://www.maa.org/external_archive/devlin/devlin_06_08.html*
https://www.maa.org/external_archive/devlin/devlin_0708_08.html
https://www.maa.org/external_archive/devlin/devlin_09_08.html
https://www.maa.org/external_archive/devlin/devlin_01_11.html

Those articles were not opinion pieces; I was simply reporting what has long been known about mathematics and math education. Yet many people reading them assumed they were, and argued vehemently, and often passionately, that I was wrong. But arguing based on your *existing beliefs* is the worst thing to do in education. Learning is about looking at the evidence, reflecting on it, cross-checking to ensure veracity of reporting, and then adjusting your knowledge and beliefs accordingly. If you are not discovering that you were wrong, or that you did not properly understand something, then *you are not learning*. Period.

Enter Denise into the fray. (It was actually more like a firestorm at the time.) Her July 1, 2008 post on Let's Play Math, which she wrote right after she read the first of my multiplication-is-not-repeated-addition posts, was one of the best illustrations of how the mathematics learning process *should* progress I have ever seen. Check it out, paying particular attention to her *process*. She came back to the topic in two subsequent posts.[†]

In the months and years that followed, we had a (small) number of email exchanges, and followed each other's writings. She read me because I had devoted much of my life to mathematics, and *how to express it* so as to make some of its deeper complexities accessible to a wider audience; I read her because she had devoted much of her life to *how to teach it* to younger people so that they can learn it. Teaching is not instruction, though many fail to see the distinction. Teaching is creating the circumstances in which a person can learn. In the education domain, I am primarily an instructor; Denise is a teacher. We learned from each other, bringing different experiences and different perspectives.

Which brings me back to my opening comments. We are used to assigning labels such as "mathematician", "teacher", "writer", "doctor", "accountant", "journalist", etc., based on established credentials. This gives us a way to quickly judge how we should approach such individuals and whether to put our faith in what they say.

But in today's digitally-connected world, there is another path to achieving "professional" status. Instead of convincing a small number of people (examiners, editors, etc.) that we merit such approval, with each of

---

† *http://denisegaskins.com/2008/07/01/if-it-aint-repeated-addition*
http://denisegaskins.com/2008/07/28/whats-wrong-with-repeated-addition/
http://denisegaskins.com/2012/07/16/pufm-1-5-multiplication-part-1

those gatekeepers having undergone the same vetting process, now anyone can set themselves up as whatever they choose, put out or promote their work on the Internet, and then let the so-called "Wisdom of the Crowd" make the call.

It's a process fraught with dangers (so was the old system), and open to abuse and manipulation (so was the old system). But as Wikipedia showed, when it works it can be every bit as good as, if not better than, the old system.

Since anyone can play, this alternative approach is undoubtedly much more democratic than the older, establishment framework. The problem— and it is a big one—is that in the ocean of activity that is the Internet, it is hard for a truly talented individual to get their work noticed.

If it were not for the chance occurrence that Bill Gates stumbled across Salman Khan's online math instruction videos when he was trying to help his son with his math homework, Khan Academy would likely still be one of many largely unknown websites offering math tutorial videos. Were it not for Dan Meyer having been invited to give a TEDtalk that went viral, he would likely be to this day one of many blogging math teachers. And we can all think of other examples.

It's not that Sal Khan and Dan Meyer were not doing something of value. Rather, it required a stroke of luck to bring them to the attention of someone who could propel them far enough for their own talent to do the rest.

Denise's Let's Play Math blog, which is approaching 1,000 posts at the time of my writing this foreword (early 2016), gets around 40,000 page views per month (about 25,000 visitors), with about 1,300 blog feed subscribers. That's a successful blog. But it's nothing like where it should be in terms of the interest and quality of the posts.

Well, I'm not Bill Gates, nor do I control who gets invited to give TEDtalks. But insofar as I have some degree of name recognition in the math world, I'd like to use it to try to bring Denise Gaskins's work to a wider audience. That's why I offered to write this foreword and to promote her book in my various writings. It may not be enough; but I want to give it a try. [Note to other authors. Pitching me is not likely to work. Denise and I have been exchanging emails since 2008. She sent me a copy of her manuscript only after I requested it, which I did after she emailed me asking my permission to include a short passage from Devlin's Angle.]

At the time I am writing these words, the first edition of this book sits at position 315,714 in the Amazon ranking of paid Kindle books. Based on its quality, it should be much higher.

On the other hand, the first edition is (again at the time of writing) in the Top 100 in the Education & Teaching/Teacher Resources/Parent Participation category.

Take note of that categorization. Largely through her blog, Denise is known in the homeschooling community (though not exclusively so). And that is no small community. According to the US Department of Education's National Center for Education Statistics (NCES) 2013 report, just under 2 million students were being homeschooled in the US at the time, roughly 3.5% of the school-age population. That figure has surely grown since then.[†]

Parents homeschool for a variety of reasons, and do so with a wide range of abilities, doubtless with a wide range of success. For many, maybe most, mathematics presents a particularly difficult challenge. Dramatic changes in society and the workplace resulting from new computational technologies have rendered irrelevant much of the math it was important for my generation to learn, while at the same time making other math skills now critically important. I'm not referring just to "math content" here. The way we think about mathematics—the way we approach it— has changed. The emphasis used to be—correctly—on mastery of a set of procedures. Today, when we have access to all the resources on the Internet and have cheap devices in our pockets that can carry out those procedures faster and much more accurately than the human brain, the critical math abilities are conceptually sound mathematical thinking and creative problem solving, making use of the technologies to carry out the procedural parts. (Arguably good collaboration and communication skills are equally important, but they are of a different nature.)

Unfortunately, when it comes to mathematics, many homeschooling parents have little recourse other than fall back on how they themselves learned in school (or all too often, *failed* to learn in school). Even if they realize that they owe their children more, they don't know where to find it or how to evaluate what they find. Show me a math resource you pick

---

† *http://nces.ed.gov/pubsearch/pubsinfo.asp?pubid=2013316*

on the Web at random and I'll likely be able to point out a whole host of damaging errors of different kinds.

Denise knows what is involved in being a homeschooling parent. As a result, I would hope that other homeschoolers will take note of what she says. What is significant in her case, and is definitely not the case for many of the homeschooling parents I have met and interacted with over the years, is that she understands the mathematics and what is involved in teaching it.

Does she know it all? No. Neither do I. Is she always right? No. Neither am I. But neither of those matter. Mathematics is not about knowing or being right. It is about wanting to know and wanting to be right. It is about how we think about things, how we react to discovering we are wrong, and how we learn new things —new concepts, new facts, new procedures. It is about approaching everything with an open mind. It is about recognizing that doing math means constantly feeling we are about to fall off the cliff of comprehension, but approaching it in a want-to-win, playful way that lets us enjoy that "fear."

Let's Play Math: How Families Can Learn Math Together and Enjoy It is a special book. Its very title captures what I think is its most important feature: the book is a rich resource of ideas and activities for parents to explore and work through with their children. Written by a great writer who has been doing exactly that for many years.

"Math is not just rules and rote memory," Denise says. "Math is like ice cream, with more flavors than you can imagine. And if all you ever do is textbook math, that's like eating broccoli-flavored ice cream."

Enjoy (with your children) the fayre that Denise Gaskins serves up. After all, how often do you get an opportunity to feast—every day—on a family dessert that is highly nutritious and will help set your kids up for life?

—Keith Devlin
Palo Alto, CA
January 30, 2016

Preface to the Paperback Edition

As a young parent and newbie homeschooler, I tried to fit my children's education into the only model of school I knew. Textbooks, daily schedules, and slogging through one tedious workbook after another made education seem boring, when it ought to be a lifelong adventure. As my children grew, I noticed how much learning happened outside of "school" time, through library books or life experiences. We moved to a more relaxed, eclectic mentoring style. We discovered that even a math textbook can be fun when used as a source of puzzles.

On a daily basis, homeschoolers, tutors, and parents simply trying to help with homework experience the truth of the adage "The teacher learns more than the students." I've been learning more than my children for three decades now, and helping other parents learn more than their children for almost that long.

My math books began as handouts for my workshops and conference talks, folded and stapled by hand. When they grew too big for the stapler, I published them as simple, comb-bound paperbacks in the late-1990s. After those went out of print, I started my Let's Play Math blog to provide extra resources for my workshop participants. The old books sprouted as blog posts, fertilized by new tips, updated examples, and hands-on activities.

Through my blog, I discovered a wider audience. All parents, whatever their school (or unschool) affiliation, naturally want their children to enjoy learning. They are hungry for creative, playful ways to approach math. To my surprise, classroom teachers also were interested in what a homeschool mom had to share. We all face the same struggle: to explain abstract concepts in a way that young minds can grasp.

Meanwhile, four of my children grew up and graduated. My youngest is now in high school. After so many years of parenting, I'm still learning and thinking to myself, "I've got to share this!" So I mixed the fruits of my blog—revised games, creative projects, fresh insights—back into this *Let's Play Math* book and the *Math You Can Play* series. I've fixed all the typos I could find, deleted obsolete references, and served it all up with a tasty buffet of math books and Internet resources.

I hope my books help to make math your children's favorite subject. If you have any questions, please drop me a note.

—Denise Gaskins
Blue Mound, IL
November17, 2016
LetsPlayMath@gmail.com

Acknowledgments

No one is an island, and authors perhaps less than most. I cannot possibly express the debt I owe to the family, friends, and online acquaintances whose help and support have made this book possible. Special thanks to my husband David, whose patience stretches far beyond what I deserve, and our children, who taught me so much over the many years of homeschooling.

Thank you to Marilyn Kok, who pushed me to write way back in the beginning, to Julie Pangrac, who talked me into doing workshops for homeschool groups, and to Sue VanHattum, whose work on her own book, *Playing with Math: Stories from Math Circles, Homeschoolers, and Passionate Teachers,* convinced me to bring my books back into print. To my many thousands of book and blog readers, your comments and encouragement have kept me going. To my fellow math bloggers, I've learned so much from you all.

Fervent thanks to my beta readers: Becky, Jenny, Maria, Sheryl, and Sue. Your comments made the book so much better than I could do alone. And a huge mound of gratitude (with whipped cream and caramel topping) to my editors Jim Mcfarlin and Elizabeth Sheley—whatever mistakes remain are due to my continual tinkering after the file left their hands.

Our own experience with
introducing advanced math to little kids
tells us that it can be difficult.

Surprisingly, the difficulty is not
in getting the kids
to understand the concepts.

Instead, it's the difficulty
in getting the non-mathematician parents
to believe that math can be fun
and to see it all around us.
After years and years of traditional math learning,
many parents find it hard to think of math
as something other than numbers.

Sure, math does deal with numbers.
But limiting mathematics to numbers
is like limiting parenting to changing diapers.

—Yelena McManaman

How to
Understand Math

It is in fact nothing short of a miracle that the modern methods of instruction have not entirely strangled the holy curiosity of inquiry; for this delicate little plant, aside from stimulation, stands mainly in need of freedom.

—ALBERT EINSTEIN

Introduction

A CUP OF COFFEE, A slice of pecan pie, and a robust discussion of educational philosophy—when I was a novice homeschooler, our local moms' night out provided mentoring and kept me sane. Years passed. Children grew. Many of the kids we worried over then are now raising children of their own. Though I can't remember growing older, I look in the mirror and find a gray-haired veteran.

I'd love to sit down with you for an afternoon's chat or an evening at the coffee shop, but our "night out" will have to be virtual. So I'll sip at my cup while I write. Perhaps you can nibble a bit of pie as you read. And together let's ponder the problem of learning math.

Our childhood struggles with schoolwork left many of us wary of mathematics. We learned to manipulate numbers and recite basic facts and formulas, but we never saw how or why it all fit together. We stumbled from one class to the next, packing ever more information into our strained memory, until the whole structure threatened to collapse. Eventually we crashed in a blaze of confusion, some of us in high school algebra, others in college calculus. If this is your experience, you may be wondering how you can possibly help your children learn math. Don't worry, you can! I'll show you that doing math together is easier than you think, and an awful lot of fun for both you and your children.

3

Before plunging in, let's take a moment to think about education.

Everyone has a philosophy of education, though they may not have thought it through. We've all been taught. There were parts of our schooling we liked and other parts we'd like to have changed. Over the years—in books, on websites and parenting forums, and in personal discussions—I've heard a range of opinions about how children learn math. Take a look at the list of statements I've collected, and think about the education you want for your children.

Which of the following points would you say are true? Which are math myths?

- ♦ Mathematics means the rules for working with numbers, shapes, and algebraic symbols.
- ♦ Math is in the genes. Some people have a "math mind," but most of us don't.
- ♦ Math is logical and rigid, not creative or artistic.
- ♦ Math is timeless and objective. It's the same for everyone.
- ♦ In mathematics, answers are either right or wrong. The right answer is never a matter of opinion.
- ♦ To do well at math, you need a good memory.
- ♦ Learning mathematics is like climbing a ladder. You have to master the basics before you can reach the higher rungs.
- ♦ Children need a textbook or workbook to learn math.
- ♦ Looking at someone else's answer is cheating.
- ♦ Students should show all the steps of their work. Shortcuts will lead to mistakes.
- ♦ Children shouldn't count on their fingers.
- ♦ Children need to memorize the times tables. They should drill the math facts until they can answer flashcard-fast.

These statements sum up the way many adults remember school mathematics. Yet they are all math myths. Not one of these statements is indisputably true.

Could these myths be the reason why so many children learn to hate math? Or why so many parents feel inadequate to help their kids?

"There is a huge elephant standing in most math classrooms," says Stanford University math education professor Jo Boaler. "It is the idea that only some students can do well in math. Students believe it, parents believe and teachers believe it. The myth that math is a gift that some students have and some do not, is one of the most damaging ideas that pervades education in the US and that stands in the way of students' math achievement."

Unfortunately, math myths don't just stand there peacefully. Like a wild animal caught in a small room, they stamp and trample and wreak havoc on a child's confidence. Before we can help our children learn math, we need to chase these myths away.

Mathematics is much more than a set of rules. Contrary to popular perception, it can be very artistic. Unlike traditional school work, real math poses intriguing questions, making us want to explore its patterns and puzzles. As we play alongside our children, we can share the satisfaction of discovering why things work.

Yes, there are advanced topics that can be hard to understand. Some math problems are fiendishly difficult. Yet the basic principles of math—even at the high school level—grow from common sense. Learning them should feel natural.

Math is not the same for everyone, because what you see depends on your point of view. There are also different kinds of math. For example, can you draw a pair of parallel lines? In some versions of geometry, parallel lines do not exist. Does $2 + 2 = 4$? Not always: in modular arithmetic $2 + 2 = 0 \mod 4$, while in base three $2 + 2 = 11$. These topics can be interesting to explore with your children. Finding new ways to look at familiar ideas is part of the joy of learning math as a family.

A few of the myths in my list may have a semblance of truth, but their cumulative effect is to limit our children's understanding and ability to appreciate math. Many later math topics do build on earlier ones, but learning math is more like taking a meandering nature walk than like climbing a ladder with one rung above another. Preschool children are capable of exploring topics like fractals or infinity, while elementary students can begin learning algebra. It's fun to play with advanced ideas. Such

Modular arithmetic works like a one-handed clock. In mod 4, moving 2 + 2 brings you back around to zero. And 2 + 3 isn't five, because that number doesn't exist in mod 4. Instead, you keep moving around the clock, so 2 + 3 = 1. How many other mod 4 math facts can you find?

adventures offer a broad perspective that supports a child's knowledge of the more standard arithmetic topics.

Even with the basics of *arithmetic* (number calculations, the traditional focus of elementary school math), the ladder analogy hurts more than it helps. Young children need freedom to wander from one topic to another as interest and opportunity lead them. They can ponder the concepts of multiplication and fractions long before they have finished mastering addition and subtraction.

Nor is a textbook necessary, at least during the early-elementary years. Most young children have a natural interest in mathematical ideas as part of their ongoing mission to understand and control their world. They find numbers fascinating, especially big numbers like hundreds or thousands. They enjoy drawing circles and triangles. They delight in scooping up volumes in the sandbox or bathtub. They can count out forks and knives for the table, matching sets of silverware with the resident set of people. They know how to split up the last bit of birthday cake and make sure they get their fair share, even if they have to cut halves or thirds.

Homeschoolers are not immune to math myths. When I was a child, all teachers exhorted us to "Show your work." I've seen many homeschooling discussion forum posts asking how parents can convince kids to write out the steps of their answers. Yet our teachers were not really interested in our childish pencil-scratchings; what they wanted was a window into how we were thinking. As parents, we have an advantage that classroom teachers can only dream of—namely, the time to sit and talk with each of our children. I can ask my daughter, "How did you figure it out?" In the course of conversation, she will demonstrate how much she knows. I often find myself learning something from the discussion, too, since she almost never thinks a problem through in the same way I would have done. I'd hate to trade this opportunity for a notebook page full of written-out steps.

Or consider the idea that looking at someone else's answer is cheating. While that is undoubtedly true during a test, such pressure should be rare. Wise parents and teachers know that children need to hear many different ways to approach a problem. They need to compare their solutions with others. When students are stumped on a math exercise, one of the best ways to learn is to look up the answer and work backward.

The last statement in my list of math myths—that children should memorize their times tables and practice until they can answer flashcard-fast—is the most controversial. With our modern culture's infatuation with test scores, many people will argue, "That's not a myth!" Frantic parents scour the Internet, desperate for tricks that will help their kids learn the math facts. But for many children, this emphasis on memory work does more harm than good. While understanding the meaning of multiplication is vital, instant recall is like icing on a brownie: tasty, but unnecessary. When we stress memorization, we risk short-circuiting our child's learning process. Once kids "know" an answer, they no longer

In base 3, the place value columns are multiples of three. Instead of writing numbers in terms of ones, tens, and hundreds, we count by ones, threes, and nines. Thus 2 + 2 = 11, because "11" means "one three and one single block." How many other base three facts can you find?

bother to think about it. It's better for them to spend more time in the "thinking about it" stage, where they can build a logical foundation for mastery not merely of the math facts but of many future topics as well.

Let's Play Math will show you how to build on your children's natural attraction to mathematical ideas. Even if you don't know much about mathematics—even if you had a terrible childhood experience of school math, even if the idea of fractions or long division makes you feel like throwing up—you can help your children master math. There's always time to make a fresh start. We adults can learn right along with our kids.

So turn the page, and let's explore what it means to understand math as a game. Along the way, you will discover practical ways to weave informal, playful math into your everyday lives, develop problem-solving skills, and bring math alive by exploring history. You'll find out how to deal with many of the common struggles children face and meet a wealth of resources to help you on your educational journey. Most of all, you will see how people of all ages can enjoy learning math together.

Links and Resources

All of the books and websites I mention are listed in the "Resources and References" section at the end of this book (beginning on page 211), or you can check out the resource pages on my blog:
http://denisegaskins.com/living-math-books
http://denisegaskins.com/internet-math-resources

The website links in this book were checked in December 2015, but the Internet is volatile. If a website disappears, you can run a browser search for the author's name or article title. Or try entering the web address at the Internet Archive Wayback Machine.
http://archive.org/web/web.php

1

If a child is to keep alive his inborn sense of wonder, he needs the companionship of at least one adult who can share it, rediscovering with him the joy, excitement, and mystery of the world we live in.
—RACHEL CARSON

The "Aha!" Factor

I SAT ON THE BED, surrounded by stacks of notes, bills, and other papers. Our six-year-old bounced onto the other side.

"Mom, can we do some math?" she asked.

We delay academics, so I had not planned to do schoolwork with her at all. I suppose she was jealous of what she saw as her older siblings' Mommy-time.

I started to say I was busy, but stopped myself in mid-grumble. *You do that too often,* I scolded myself. I forced a smile.

"OK," I said. "Let's see what we can find."

I put the most important papers to the side. We counted the items that remained, then took some away and counted again.

Then I leaned over and whispered in her ear. "Guess what? We made cookies, just for you and me. And we're not going to share them with the big kids."

Her eyes grew wide. "Really?"

I told her we had six (imaginary) cookies. I piled up two notebooks, a used envelope, a sheet of scratch paper, a computer printout, and my pen. She divided the "cookies" between us. We giggled as we pretended to eat. Then she picked out seven new cookies for me to divide. I made exaggerated motions of cutting the electric bill in half. We counted things one by one and in pairs, paying attention to which numbers came out even and which numbers made us cut up the last cookie.

After ten minutes she went away happy, and I returned to my work. Subtraction, division, even and odd numbers, fractions, … in that short time, we had touched on more math than we might have found in a week's worth of workbook pages.

For young children, mathematical concepts are part of life's daily adventure. Their minds grapple with understanding abstract ideas such as *threeness:* the intangible yet real link between three blocks and three fingers and three raisins on a plate. But after a few sessions of "3 + 1 = 4, 3 + 2 = 5, 3 + 3 …" they begin to whine. Older children recoil from long division. High school students face torture like this: "The product of an integer and the next greater integer is 20 less than the square of the greater integer." Math becomes a tedious chore to put off as long as possible or to finish with slapdash speed.

Mathematics ought to be a game of discovery. It should give children the same *Eureka!* thrill that sent Archimedes running through town in his birthday suit. I call this the "Aha!" factor, the delight of solving a challenging puzzle. I aim for this "Aha!" factor when I bring home a brainteaser book from the library or a new game from the store.

The Problem with Traditional School Math

Why, as they grow up, do so many children learn to hate math? Why does the idea of math homework make so many parents feel like crying?

American mathematician Hassler Whitney once said that it is "no wonder you hate math. You never had a chance to see or do real math, which is easy and fun."

Easy? Yes, that's what he said. Of course, some parts of math can be difficult to master. Some math problems are extremely challenging. But compared to traditional school math, which requires us to memorize and recall arbitrary rules for the manipulation of abstract quantities, real mathematics is more like common sense—which makes it feel more natural.

As British mathematician, educator, and author W. W. Sawyer explained, "A widespread fallacy about teaching is the idea that remembering is easy and understanding difficult. John is a bright boy, we will teach him what the subject really means; Henry is dull, he will just have to learn things by heart. Now exactly the opposite is true: to remember things which you do not understand is extremely difficult."

Real mathematics is intriguing and full of wonder—an exploration of patterns and mysterious connections. It rewards us with the joy of the "Aha!" feeling. These characteristics make it easy to stick with real math, even when a particular concept or problem presents a difficult challenge. Workbook math, on the other hand, is several pages of long division by hand followed by a rousing chorus of the fraction song: "Ours is not to reason why, just invert and multiply."

Real math is the surprising fact that the odd numbers add up to perfect squares (1, 1 + 3, 1 + 3 + 5, etc.) and the satisfaction of seeing why it must be so. Did your algebra teacher ever explain to you that a *square number* is literally a number that can be arranged to make a square? Try it for yourself:

♦ Gather a bunch of pennies, or any small items that will not roll away when you set them out in rows. Place one of them in front of you on the table. Imagine drawing a frame around it: one penny makes a (very small) square. One row, with one item in each row.

♦ Now, put out three more pennies. How will you add them to the first one to form a new, bigger square? Arrange them in a small L-shape around the original penny to make two rows with two pennies in each row.

♦ Set out five more pennies. Without moving the current four, how can you place these five to form the next square? Three rows of three.

♦ Then how many will you have to add to make four rows of four?

Each new set of pennies must add an extra row and column to the current square, plus a corner penny where the new row and column meet. The row and column match exactly, making an even number, and then the extra penny at the corner makes it odd. Can you see that the "next odd number" pattern will continue as long as there are pennies to add? And that it could keep going forever in your imagination?

Twenty-five is a square number, because we can arrange twenty-five items to make a square: five rows with five items in each row.

The point of the penny square is not to memorize the square numbers or to get any particular "right answer," but to see numbers in a new way. To understand that numbers are related to each other. To realize we can show such relationships with diagrams or physical models. The more relationships like this our children explore, the more they see numbers as familiar friends.

A focus on answer-getting and test performance can ruin mathematics, distorting a discipline that is half art and half sport. Imagine a piano teacher who insisted her students spend six years on scales and exercises of gradually increasing difficulty before she would let them attempt a piece of actual music. Or a football coach who made his team run laps and do sit-ups every day, but let them play only two or three games a year, and scrimmage games at that. How many people would become bored with music or learn to hate football under such instruction?

As every coach knows, skill grows through practice. But practice has no meaning unless the team has a real game to play. And the best type of practice takes advantage of the benefits of cross-training by emphasizing variety rather than repetitive drills. Mathematical cross-training will include games, puzzles, stories, patterns, physical models, and the challenge of thinking things through.

Our children do need to learn how to perform routine calculations, as piano players must practice scales and football players lift weights. More important, however, our children need to learn why those operations work. And they must never be led to think that calculations are the essence of mathematics.

"A teacher of mathematics has a great opportunity," wrote Hungarian math professor George Polya. "If he fills his allotted time with drilling his students in routine operations he kills their interest, hampers their intellectual development, and misuses his opportunity.

"But if he challenges the curiosity of his students by setting them problems proportionate to their knowledge, and helps them to solve their problems with stimulating questions, he may give them a taste for, and some means of, independent thinking."

Playing with Numbers

Writing for *Family Life* magazine, mathematician and music critic Edward Rothstein described a game he invented for his daughter:

> *"What number am I? If you add me to myself, you get four."*

I gave that question to my six-year-old daughter during a family car trip. Then her sister, age nine, wanted in the game. I tried a question with bigger numbers, but she rolled her eyes. "That's too easy, Mom."

So I asked her:

> *"What number am I? If you take away one-fourth of me and then add two, you get seventeen." [answer1]*

The older our children get, the harder their parents have to work. For my twelve-year-old son, I asked:

"What number am I? If you multiply me by myself and add one, you get half as many as the number of pennies in a dollar." [answer2]

That kept him busy for a few minutes. After he figured it out, he came back with:

"What number am I? If you divide me by two and take away four, then add five, then multiply by three and divide by two and add seven, you get me again."

"What?" I asked. He repeated the question.

"This is actually a number?" I asked. "You figured out an answer to this?"

He nodded, with the smug grin of a preteen who knows he has Mom skewered.

I pulled out a notebook and pen. He repeated his series of calculations, and this time I wrote it down. I figured the answer had to be zero or one, those magic numbers that make multiplying easy, but neither worked.

I tried one hundred. No luck.

I heard a chuckle from the back seat.

"Wait," I said. "Give me a chance."

My husband was driving, but he glanced over at the notebook. "You know," he offered, "you could set that up as an equation."

Answers

You can find "Answers to Sample Problems" in the appendixes (page 236). Problem 1 has two possible solutions, depending on how you understand the words in the question. My daughter did not see it the same way I did. Her answer caught me by surprise—it was three times the number I expected—and yet after she explained her reasoning, I had to admit that her solution, too, was correct.

Let this be a warning: if your child's answer is not the same as yours, don't assume she is wrong. Ask her to explain how she figured it out. Then listen with care. Children almost always have a logical reason for their answers. Language is a complicated thing, and even a math problem may be open to different interpretations.

No way. The boy had not needed algebra to figure it out, so neither did I. So I tried ten, then fifty, then twenty. OK, that narrowed it down. Now I knew the answer had to be between twenty and fifty, but I had run out of easy numbers.

I nibbled on the end of my pen.

My son hummed to himself.

"I've got it." I spun around as far as the seat belt allowed. "The answer is ___." [answer3]

"Nope."

"WHAT?"

I looked at my scratch paper. I worked the numbers again, coming up with the same answer. I read the steps of my calculation out loud.

He agreed that my number would work, but it was not the one he had in mind. I would have to guess again.

Hubby protested that there couldn't be another answer. If the equation doesn't have an x^2 or something similar, there can't be more than one solution.

The kid stood his ground, smirking.

I conceded. "What's your number?"

"Infinity. It doesn't matter what you multiply or take away, it's always infinity."

Aha! He was right. Well, sort of right: infinity isn't a real number, so you can't calculate with it that way. But it's good enough for middle school. Even better, he had a chance to stump the adults.

Playing with Shapes and Patterns

Even the simplest objects can provide an opportunity for mathematical play. The following story comes from math teacher Christopher Danielson, the primary organizer behind the hands-on "Math On-A-Stick" exhibit at the 2015 Minnesota State Fair.

Danielson writes …

I have spent the last four days playing and talking math with kids of all ages for eleven hours a day, paying close attention to how children behave in this space we've built. My number one message coming out of this work is *Let the children play.*

When children come to the egg table at Math On-A-Stick, they know right away what to do. There are brightly colored plastic eggs, and there are large, flat thirty-egg cartons. The eggs go in the cartons.

No one needs to give them instructions.

A typical three- or four-year old will fill the cartons haphazardly. She won't be concerned with the order she fills it, nor with the colors she uses, nor anything else. She'll just put eggs into the carton one at a time in a seemingly random order.

But when that kid plays a second or third time, emptying and filling her egg carton—without being told to do so—she usually begins to see new possibilities. After five or ten minutes of playing eggs, this child is filling the carton in rows or columns. Or she's making patterns such as pink, yellow, pink, yellow, and so on. Or she's counting the eggs as she puts them in the carton. Or she's orienting all of the eggs so they are pointy-side up.

The longer the child plays, the richer the mathematical activity she engages in. This is because the materials themselves have math built into them. The rows and columns of the egg crate; the colors and shape of the eggs; the fact that the eggs can separate into halves—all of these are mathematical features that kids notice and begin to play with as they spend time at the table.

We have seen four-year-olds spend an hour playing with the eggs.

I have observed that the children who receive the least instruction from parents, volunteers, or me are the most likely to persist. These are the children who will spend twenty minutes or more exploring the possibilities in the eggs.

The children who receive instructions from adults are least likely to persist. When a parent or volunteer says, "Make a pattern," kids are likely to do one of two things:

♦ Make a pattern, quit, and move to something else.

♦ Stop playing without making a pattern.

We adults have a responsibility to let the children play. We can be there to listen to their ideas as they do. We can play in parallel by getting our own egg cartons out and filling these cartons with our own ideas.

But when we tell kids to "make a pattern" or "use the colors," we are asking the children to fill their carton with our ideas, rather than allowing them to explore their own.

—Christopher Danielson

What Is Our Goal?

As children approach school age, today's parents face a bewildering array of choices. Many find it useful to write out (or at least to talk through) their educational ideals. Is our mission like filling the empty bucket of a child's mind, or is it more like lighting a fire that will grow and spread on its own? Or is our role not to "teach" at all, but rather to walk alongside and assist our children as they explore the world? How we define our goals will make an enormous difference in how we approach the day by day adventure of learning.

In the same way, before we can figure out how to help our children with math, we need to think about our goals. What does it take to understand mathematics? Is it truly necessary for our children? After all, computers and calculators crunch most of the numbers in our modern world. Some children must grow up to program those computers, but what if my kids have other plans?

Do I want my children to learn math only because the state requires it? The state requires our children to learn math so they will be functionally literate. That may not sound like a lofty goal, but think about what "functionally literate in math" means:

- ◆ Filling out an IRS Form 1040 with its Schedule A, Schedule B, Schedule SE, and all the rest.

- ◆ Reading a mortgage and understanding how a fixed- or variable-rate loan will affect family finances.

- ◆ Following newspaper articles about the governor's budget proposal or discerning the relevance of political polls.

- ◆ Knowing that a 40% chance of rain on Saturday and a 60% chance of rain on Sunday doesn't mean there is a 100% chance of rain this weekend.

Mathematical literacy is a worthy challenge. But most of us want more than literacy for our children. We want them to be educated. An educated person is interested in more than merely what is useful. He or she loves to learn, studies for the sake of gaining knowledge, and grows in wisdom.

Few people read Shakespeare because his plays are useful. But an educated person will enjoy Shakespeare because his stories are interesting and his dialogue insightful. Likewise, much of math does not seem to be useful, but it can be fascinating.

If you want to experience the joy and artistry of math, consider *fractals*, which are intricate patterns of regular irregularity that capture something of the complex beauty in nature. The men who first discovered fractals in the late nineteenth century called them "monster curves." They could not imagine any use for such absurdities. Yet today, these monsters are used to compress images and other data files and have become a staple tool in film makers' special-effects kit.

Children who are educated in math will gain practical skills. But what is more important, those who enjoy learning for its own sake will find plenty to fascinate them.

Math the Mathematician's Way

Real mathematics is not just formulaic tutoring. My hope is that children learn to think about mathematics as a kind of mental play.
—Edward Rothstein

Mathematics is mental play, the essence of creative problem solving. This is the truth we need to impart to our children, more important than fractions or decimals or even the times tables. Math is a game, playing with ideas.

Traditional school math is a lock-step sequence of topics, but math the mathematician's way is a social adventure of exploring and sharing new ideas. Math the mathematician's way is fun. It can even be beautiful. Listen to how real mathematicians, both professionals and amateurs who enjoy working with math, describe their subject:

I love mathematics principally because it is beautiful, because man has breathed his spirit of play into it, and because it has given him his

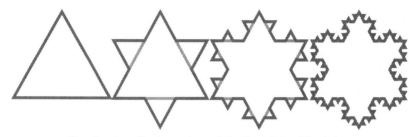

Step by step, the boundary of the Koch Island fractal—
sometimes called the Koch Snowflake—approaches infinite
raggedness, much as an actual coastline appears more
and more jagged under increasing magnification.

By allowing random variation as they design a
fractal, artists can create natural-looking forms such
as this mountainous coastline in winter.

greatest game—the encompassing of the infinite.
—RÓZSA PÉTER

There is no ulterior practical purpose here. I'm just playing. That's what math is: wondering, playing, amusing yourself with your imagination.
—PAUL LOCKHART

Puzzles in one sense, better than any other single branch of mathematics, reflect its always youthful, unspoiled, and inquiring spirit. When a man stops wondering and asking and playing, he is through.
—EDWARD KASNER

If mathematics education communicated this playful aspect of the subject, I don't think innumeracy would be as widespread as it is.
—JOHN ALLEN PAULOS

W. W. Sawyer wrote a book called *Mathematician's Delight,* in which he described mathematical thinking this way: "Everyone knows that it is easy to do a puzzle if someone has told you the answer. That is simply a test of memory. You can claim to be a mathematician only if you can solve puzzles that you have never studied before. That is the test of reasoning."

It is also the test of life. Every day we face puzzles we have not studied before. Math taught the mathematician's way prepares us to approach problems with confidence. It teaches us to see our mistakes as stepping stones to learning. It reminds us that there may be more than one right answer, as my children and I discovered when we played "What Number Am I?"

Math taught the mathematician's way gives our children practice struggling with challenging problems. It lets them enjoy that "Aha!" thrill when they find a solution. Math the mathematician's way prepares them for careers or college. It gives them tools they can use throughout their lives. It gives them confidence by letting them succeed at something difficult. When kids solve a puzzle that stumped their parents, they know they can handle anything.

Children who play around with math taught the mathematician's way may not follow the schedule demanded by their state's math standards. If we de-emphasize worksheets, timed drills, and anxiety-producing tests, we can encourage our children to focus on reasoning skills and thinking

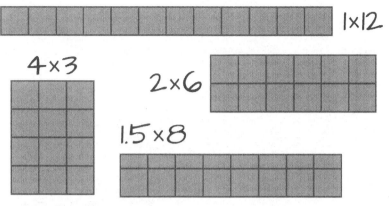

1×12

4×3

2×6

1.5×8

Math with many right answers: how long are the sides
of a rectangle with an area of twelve squares?

a situation through. We don't need to quiz our kids on the addition facts or times tables.

Of course our children need to know how to add and subtract, multiply and divide. But wonder-inducing ideas such as Fibonacci numbers (see Fibonacci's Rabbit Problem on page 130) give students an adventure in real-world addition that goes far beyond the basic math facts. Playing around with exponential growth (see the Penny Birthday Challenge on page 68) provides experience with real-world multiplication in a way that even many adults fail to understand.

Flashcard drills and practice pages of arithmetic problems are the least effective ways to learn math. Rote learning is the laziest, most deadening way to approach any subject. Think of memorizing dates in history class, and compare that to reading historic speeches and well-written biographies. On occasion, such memory work may be necessary, but it should never be the bulk of a child's experience in any subject.

Instead, we need to introduce our students to the thrill of tackling tough, challenging puzzles. We need to give children a taste of the joy that comes from figuring things out, the "Aha!" factor. We need to adopt the mathematician's view of math as mental play. Learning to think a problem through can be hard work—and that is exactly what makes it fun.

In the late 12th century, Leonardo of Pisa—also known as Fibonacci—created a small story problem about breeding rabbits, which leads to the Fibonacci number sequence: 1, 1, 2, 3, 5, 8, 13, 21 … The rabbits in the picture are tangram puzzles (see page 56).

Most adults, including teachers, mistake showing students how to do a calculation with teaching them to understand math.

—Rick Garlikov

Think Like a Mathematician

ALL PARENTS AND TEACHERS HAVE one thing in common: we want our children to understand and be able to use math. Counting, multiplication, fractions, geometry—these topics are older than the pyramids. So why is mathematical mastery so elusive?

"The root problem is that we're all graduates of the same system," says math educator Burt Furuta. "The vast majority of us, including those with the power to shape reform, believe that if we can compute the answer, then we understand the concept; and if we can solve routine problems, then we have developed problem-solving skills."

The culture we grew up in, with all its strengths and faults, shaped our perception of math, as we in turn shape the experience of our children.

Like any human endeavor, American math education—the system I grew up in—suffers from a series of fads. I lived through the experiment with hyper-abstract New Math in the 1960s. That led to the reactionary Back to Basics movement of the 1970s and 80s. In the last part of the twentieth century, Reform Math focused on problem solving, discovery learning, and student-centered methods. But Reform Math brought calculators into elementary classrooms and de-emphasized pencil-and-paper arithmetic, setting off a "Math War" with those who argued for a more traditional approach.

At this writing, policymakers in the U.S. are debating the Common Core State Standards initiative. These guidelines attempt to blend the best parts of reform and traditional mathematics. They try to balance an emphasis on conceptual knowledge with development of procedural fluency. The "Standards for Mathematical Practice" encourage us to make sense of math problems and persevere in solving them, to give explanations for our answers, and to listen to the reasoning of others—all of which are important aspects of math as mental play.[†] But the rigid way in which the Common Core standards were imposed and the ever-increasing emphasis on standardized tests seem likely to sabotage any hope of peace in the Math Wars.

Through all the math education fads, however, one thing remains consistent. Even before they reach the schoolhouse door, children are convinced that math is all about memorizing and following arbitrary rules. Understanding math, according to popular culture—according to movie actors, TV comedians, politicians pushing "accountability," and the aunt who quizzes you on your times tables at a family gathering—means knowing which procedures to apply so you can get the correct answers.

But when mathematicians talk about understanding math, they have something different in mind. To them, mathematics is all about ideas and the relationships between them. Understanding math means seeing the patterns in these relationships: how things are connected, how they work together, and how a single change can send ripples through the system.

What Is Your Mathematical Worldview?

Educational psychologist Richard Skemp popularized the terms *instrumental understanding* and *relational understanding* to describe these two ways of looking at mathematics. It is almost as if there were two unrelated subjects. Both are called "math," but they are different from each other as American football is from the game the rest of the world calls football.

Which of the following sounds the most like your experience of school math? Which type of math are your children learning?

---

† *http://www.corestandards.org/Math/Practice*

Instrumental Understanding: Math as a Tool

Every mathematical procedure we learn is an instrument or tool for solving a certain kind of problem. To understand math means to know which tool we are supposed to use for each type of problem and how to use that tool—how to categorize the problem, remember the formula, plug in the numbers, and do the calculation. To be fluent in math means we can produce correct answers with minimal effort.

PRIMARY GOAL: to get the right answer. In math, answers are either right or wrong, and wrong answers are useless.

KEY QUESTION: "What?" What do we know? What can we do? What is the answer?

VALUES: speed and accuracy.

METHOD: memorization. Memorize math facts. Memorize definitions and rules. Memorize procedures and when to use them. Use manipulatives and mnemonics to aid memorization.

BENEFIT: testability.

Instrumental instruction focuses on the *standard algorithms* (the pencil-and-paper steps for doing a calculation) or other step-by-step procedures. This produces quick results because students can follow the teacher's directions and crank out a page of correct answers. Students like completing their assignments with minimal struggle. Parents are pleased by their children's high grades. Teachers are happy to make steady progress through the curriculum.

Unfortunately, the focus on rules can lead children to conclude that math is arbitrary and authoritarian. Also, rote knowledge tends to be fragile. All those steps are easy to confuse or forget. Thus those who see math instrumentally must include continual review of old topics and provide frequent, repetitive practice.

Relational Understanding: Math as a Connected System

Each mathematical concept is part of a web of interrelated ideas. To understand mathematics means to see at least some of this web and to use the connections we see to make sense of new ideas. Giving a correct answer without *justification* (explaining how we know it is right) is mere accounting, not mathematics. To be fluent in math means we can think of more than one way to solve a problem.

PRIMARY GOAL: to see the building blocks of each topic and how that topic relates to other concepts.

KEY QUESTIONS: "How?" and "Why?" How can we figure that out? Why do we think this is true?

VALUES: logic and justification.

METHOD: conversation. Talk about the links between ideas, definitions, and rules. Explain why you used a certain procedure, and explore alternative approaches. Use manipulatives to investigate the logic behind a technique.

BENEFIT: flexibility.

Relational instruction focuses on children's thinking and expands on their ideas. This builds the students' ability to reason logically and to approach new problems with confidence. Mistakes are not a mark of failure, but a sign that points out something we haven't yet mastered, a chance to reexamine the mathematical web. Students look forward to the "Aha!" feeling when they figure out a new concept. Such an attitude establishes a secure foundation for future learning.

Unfortunately, this approach takes time. It requires extensive personal interaction. Discussing problems. Comparing thoughts. Searching for alternate solutions. Hashing out ideas. Those who see math relationally must plan on covering fewer new topics each year, so they can spend the necessary time to draw out and explore these connections. Relational understanding is also much more difficult to assess with a standardized test.

Is There Really a Difference?

From the outside, it's impossible to tell how a person is thinking. A boy with the instrumental perspective and a girl who reasons relationally may both get the same answers on a test. Yet under the surface, in their thoughts and how they view the world, they could not be more different.

"Mathematical thinking is more than being able to do arithmetic or solve algebra problems," says Stanford University mathematician and popular author Keith Devlin. "Mathematical thinking is a whole way of looking at things, of stripping them down to their numerical, structural, or logical essentials, and of analyzing the underlying patterns."

Our mathematical worldview influences the way we present math topics to our kids. Consider, for example, the following three rules that most of us learned in middle school.

- ♦ Area of a rectangle = length × width.

- ♦ To multiply fractions, multiply the tops (numerators) to make the top of your answer. Multiply the bottoms (denominators) to make the bottom of your answer.

$$\frac{3}{4} \times \frac{5}{8} = \frac{(3 \times 5)}{(4 \times 8)} = \frac{15}{32}$$

- ♦ When you need to multiply algebra expressions, remember to FOIL. Multiply the First terms in each parenthesis. Then multiply the Outer terms. Then the Inner and Last pairs. Finally, add all those answers together.

$$(a + b)(x + y) = ax + ay + bx + by$$

While the times symbol or the word *multiply* is used in each of these situations, the procedures are completely different. How can we help our children understand and remember these rules?

Over the next several pages, we'll dig deeper into each of these math rules as we examine what it means to develop relational understanding.

Many people misunderstand the distinction between instrumental and relational understanding. They think the terms refer to surface-level, visible differences in instructional approach, but it's not that at all. It has nothing to do with our parenting or teaching style, or whether our kids are learning with a traditional textbook or through hands-on projects. It's not about using "real world" problems, except to the degree that the world around us feeds our imagination and gives us the ability to think about math concepts.

This dichotomy is all about the vision we have for our children—what we imagine mathematical success to look like. That vision may sit below the level of conscious thought, yet it shapes everything we do with math. And our children's vision for themselves shapes what they pay attention to, care about, and remember.

Area of a Rectangle

The instrumental approach to explaining such rules is for the adult to work through a few sample problems and then give the students several more for practice. In a traditional lecture-and-workbook style curriculum, students apply the formula to drawings on paper. Under a more progressive reform-style program, the students may try to invent their own methods before the teacher provides the standard rule, or they may measure and calculate real-world areas such as the surface of their desks or the floor of their room. Either way, the ultimate goal is to define terms and master the formula as a tool to calculate answers.

Richard Skemp describes a typical lesson:

> *Suppose that a teacher reminds a class that the area of a rectangle is given by $A = L \times B$. A pupil who has been away says he does not understand, so the teacher gives him an explanation along these lines. "The formula tells you that to get the area of a rectangle, you multiply the length by the breadth."*
>
> *"Oh, I see," says the child, and gets on with the exercise.*
>
> *If we were now to say to him (in effect) "You may think you understand, but you don't really," he would not agree. "Of course I do.*

Look; I've got all these answers right."

Nor would he be pleased at our devaluing of his achievement. And with his meaning of the word, he does understand.

As the lesson moves along, students will learn additional rules. For instance, if a rectangle's length is given in meters and the width in centimeters, we must convert them both to the same units before we calculate the area. Also, our answer will not have the same units as our original lengths, but that unit with a little, floating "2" after it, which we call "squared." Each lesson may be followed by a section on word problems, so the students can apply their newly learned rules to real-life situations.

In contrast, a relational approach to area must begin long before the lesson on rectangles. Again, this can happen in a traditional, teacher-focused classroom or in a progressive, student-oriented environment. Either way, the emphasis is on uncovering and investigating the conceptual connections that lie under the surface and support the rules.

We start by exploring the concept of measurement. Our children measure a path along the floor, sidewalk, or anywhere we could imagine moving in a straight line. We learn to add and subtract such distances. Even if our path turns a corner or if we first walk forward and then double back, it's easy to figure out how far we have gone.

But something strange happens when we consider distances in two different directions at the same time. Measuring the length and width of the dining table automatically creates an invisible grid. In measuring the length of a rectangular table, we do not find just one point at any given distance. There is a whole line of points that are one foot, two feet, or three feet from the left side of the table.

And measuring the width shows us all the points that are one, two, or three feet from the near edge. Now our rectangular table is covered by virtual graph paper with squares the size of our measuring unit.

The length of the rectangle tells us how many squares we have in each row. The width tells us how many rows there are. As we imagine this invisible grid, we can see why multiplying those two numbers will tell us how many squares there are in all. That is what the word *area* means. The area of a tabletop is the number of virtual-graph-paper squares it takes to cover it up, which is why our answer will be measured in square units.

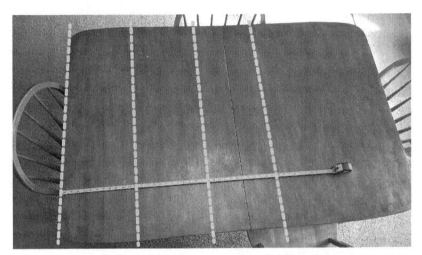

Measuring the distance from one edge of a table. Apologies
to my metric-speaking readers, but the old-fashioned foot
is the most convenient unit for this demonstration.

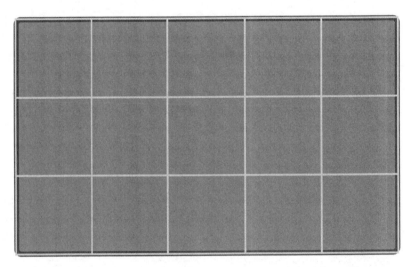

The rectangular tabletop with an imaginary grid that shows the
length and width measurements: three feet wide by five feet long.

What if we measured the length in meters and the width in centimeters? With a relational understanding of area, even a strange combination of units can make sense. Our invisible grid would no longer consist of squares but of long, thin, rectangular centimeter-meters. But we could still find the area of the tabletop by counting how many of these units it takes to cover it. Square units aren't magic—they're just easier, that's all.

How many rectangles will we need to cover a table that is
2 m long by 90 cm wide? 2 × 90 = 180 centimeter-meters.

Multiplying Fractions

Fractions inspire more math phobia among children (and adults) than any other topic before algebra. Children begin learning fractions by coloring or cutting up paper shapes. Their intuition is shaped by experiences with food like sandwiches or pizza. But before long, the abstraction of written calculations looms up to swallow intuitive understanding.

Upper elementary and middle school classrooms devote many hours to working with fractions, and still students flounder. In desperation, parents and teachers resort to nonsensical mnemonic rhymes that just might stick in a child's mind long enough to pass the test.

How can we make sense of the fraction rules?

Let's go back to our rectangular tabletop, and this time we'll zoom in. Imagine magnifying our virtual grid to show a close-up of a single square unit, such as the pan of brownies on our table. We can imagine subdividing this square into smaller, fractional pieces. In this way, we see that five-eighths of a square unit looks something like a pan of brownies cut into strips, with a few strips missing:

But what if we don't even have that whole five-eighths of the pan? Imagine that the kids came through the kitchen and snatched a few more pieces. Now all we have is three-fourths of the five-eighths.

So three-fourths of five-eighths is a small rectangle of single-serving pieces. How much of the original pan of brownies do we have now?

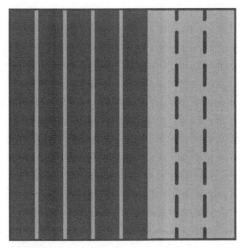

One batch of brownies is one square unit, but part of the batch has been eaten. Now we have fractional brownies: five-eighths of the pan.

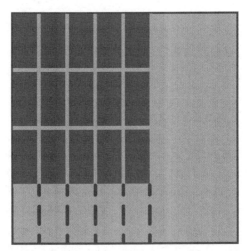

¾ of ⅝. We can make a fraction of a fraction by cutting the other direction. In this case, we cut the strips into fourths, and the kids ate one part of each strip.

There are three rows with five pieces in each row, for a total of 3 × 5 = 15 pieces left—which is the numerator of our answer. With pieces that size, it would take four rows with eight in each row (4 × 8 = 32) to fill the whole pan—which is our denominator, the number of pieces in the whole batch of brownies.

Notice that there was nothing special about the fractions ¾ and ⅝, except that the numbers were small enough for easy illustration. We could imagine a similar pan-of-brownies approach to any fraction multiplication problem, though the final pieces might turn out to be crumbs.

Children won't draw brownie-pan pictures for every fraction multiplication problem the rest of their lives. But they do need to spend plenty of time thinking about what it means to take a fraction of a fraction and how that meaning controls the numbers in their calculation. They need to ask questions, model situations, put things in their own words, and wrestle with the concept until it makes sense to them. Only then will their understanding be strong enough to support future learning.

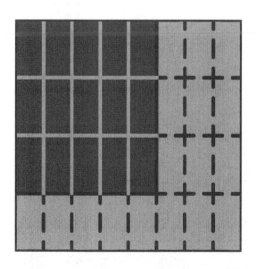

Compare the pieces we have left to the original batch. Each of the numbers in the fraction calculation has meaning. Can you find them all in the picture?

$$\frac{3}{4} \times \frac{5}{8} = \frac{(3 \times 5)}{(4 \times 8)} = \frac{15}{32}$$

Algebraic Multiplication

Let's extend the rectangle concept even further. In the connected system of mathematics, almost any type of multiplication can be imagined as a rectangular area. We don't even have to know the size of our rectangle. It could be anything, such as subdividing a plot of land or designing a section of crisscrossed colors on plaid fabric.

We can imagine a rectangle with each side made up of two unknown lengths. One side has some length a attached to another length b. The other side is x units long, with an extra amount y stuck to its end.

We don't know which side is the "length" or which is the "width" because we don't know which numbers the letters represent. But multiplication works in any order, so it doesn't matter which side is longer. Using the rectangle model of multiplication, we can see that this whole shape represents the area $(a + b)(x + y)$.

But since each side is measured in two parts, we can also imagine cutting up the big rectangle. The large, original rectangle covers the same amount of area as the four smaller rectangular pieces added together. Thus we can see that $(a + b)(x + y) = ax + ay + bx + by$.

At the beginning of this section, I gave you three middle-school math rules. But by exploring the concept of rectangular area as a model of multiplication, we discover that in a way they were all the same. The rules are not arbitrary, handed down from a mathematical Mount Olympus. They are three expressions of a single basic question: what does it mean to measure area? There was only one rule, one foundational pattern that tied all these topics together in a mathematical web.

Many children want to learn math instrumentally, as a tool for getting answers. They prefer the simplicity of memorizing rules to the more difficult task of making sense of new ideas. Being young, they are by nature short-term thinkers. They beg, "Just tell me what to do."

But if we want our children to understand math the mathematician's way, we need to resist such shortcuts. We must take time to explore mathematics as a world of ideas that connect and relate to each other in many ways. And we need to show children how to reason about these interconnected concepts, so they can use them to think their way through an ever-expanding variety of problems.

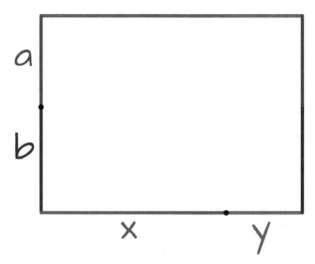

An algebraic rectangle: each side is composed of
two unknown lengths joined together.

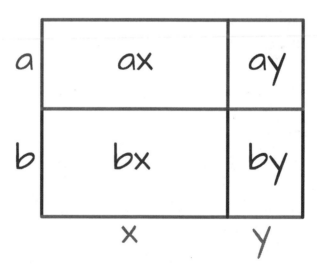

Four algebraic rectangles: the whole thing
is equal to the sum of its parts.

With the memorized FOIL formula mentioned earlier, for example, our students may get a correct answer quickly, but it's a dead end. FOIL doesn't connect to any other math concepts, not even other forms of algebraic multiplication. But the rectangular area model will help our kids multiply more complicated algebraic expressions such as $(a + b + c)$ times $(w + x + y + z)$.

Not only that, but the rectangle model gives students a tool for making sense of later topics such as polynomial division. And it is fundamental to understanding integral calculus.

Our kids can only see the short term. If we adults hope to help them learn math, our primary challenge is to guard against viewing the mastery of facts and procedures as an end in itself. We must never fall into thinking that the point of studying something is just to get the right answers. We understand this in other school subjects. Nobody imagines that the point of reading is to answer comprehension questions. We know that there is more to learning history than winning a game of Trivial Pursuit. But when it comes to math, too many parents (and far too many politicians) act as though the goal of our children's education is to produce high scores on a standardized test.

	w	x	y	z
a	aw	ax	ay	az
b	bw	bx	by	bz
c	cw	cx	cy	cz

The rectangle model of multiplication helps students keep track of all the pieces in a complex algebraic calculation.

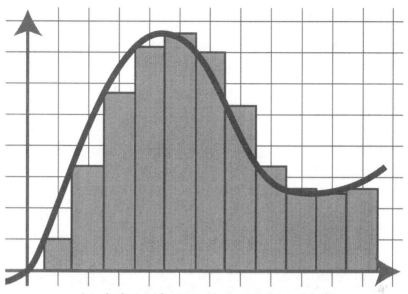

In calculus, students use the rectangle model of multiplication to find irregular areas. The narrower the rectangles, the more accurate the calculation, so we imagine shrinking the widths until they are infinitely thin.

What If I Don't Understand Math?

If you grew up (as I did) thinking of math as a tool, the instrumental approach may feel natural to you. The idea of math as a cohesive system may feel intimidating. How can we parents help our children learn math, if we never understood it this way ourselves?

Don't panic. Changing our worldview is never easy, yet even parents who suffer from math anxiety can learn to enjoy math with their children. All it takes is a bit of self-discipline and the willingness to try. You don't have to know all the answers. In fact, many people have found the same thing that Christopher Danielson described in Chapter 1 (page 15)—the more we adults tell about a topic, the less our children learn. With the best of intentions we provide information, but we unwittingly kill their curiosity.

If you're afraid of math, be careful to never let a discouraging word pass your lips. Call upon your acting skills to pretend that math is the most exciting topic in the world. Encourage your children to notice the math all around them. Investigate, experiment, estimate, explore, measure—and talk about it all. Curl up together on the couch to read a math book, or tell math stories at bedtime. Search out opportunities to discuss numbers, shapes, symmetry, and patterns with your kids.

Patterns are so important that American mathematician Lynn Arthur Steen defined mathematics as *the science of patterns*.

"As biology is the science of life and physics the science of energy and matter, so mathematics is the science of patterns," Steen wrote. "We live in an environment steeped in patterns—patterns of numbers and space, of science and art, of computation and imagination. Patterns permeate the learning of mathematics, beginning when children learn the rhythm of counting and continuing through times tables all the way to fractals and binomial coefficients."

If you are intimidated by numbers, you can look for patterns of shape and color. Pay attention to how they grow. Talk about what your children notice. For example, some patterns repeat exactly, while other patterns change as they go (small, smaller, smallest, or loud, louder, loudest). Nature often forms fractal-like patterns—the puffy round-upon-roundness of cumulus clouds or broccoli, or the branch-upon-branchiness of a shrub or river delta. Children can learn to recognize these, not as a homework exercise but because they are interesting.

Here is the secret solution to the crisis of math education: we adults need to learn how to think like mathematicians.

- ◆ Mathematicians avoid busywork as if it were an infectious disease.
- ◆ Mathematicians always ask questions.
- ◆ Most of all, mathematicians love to play.

As we cultivate these characteristics, we will help our children to recognize and learn true mathematics.

Mathematicians Avoid Busywork

Mathematicians are economical with their time and energy. You might even say they are "lazy." They have too many interesting topics to study and not enough time to learn about them all, so they cannot afford to waste their time on mindless busywork.

Mathematicians are always looking for a simpler way to do things. Skip counting is faster than addition; multiplication is even easier. Algebraic functions are shorthand ways to describe how things grow and change. Calculus lets engineers solve problems that would be impossible without it.

Some problems have more potential solutions than anyone could list, so mathematicians invented special ways to think about counting. *Permutations* let us count the possibilities when the order matters: "How many different ways might we award the first, second, and third place prizes in an art show?" *Combinations* count the ways to do something when order doesn't matter: "How many different three-person committees might we choose to plan the party for our neighborhood co-op?" Both types of puzzle can be interesting for middle school or older students.

When we look at education through the lens of mathematical laziness, we will be skeptical about the value of repetitive practice problems. If our children keep forgetting how to do certain calculations, perhaps they are not yet developmentally ready to learn them. One of the biggest problems in math education is how often we train kids to do "number

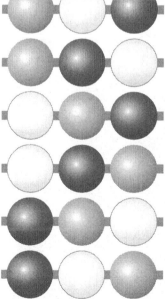

tricks" the same way we would train a dog to fetch or roll over, by having them repeat the procedure until they can do it without thinking. Children will master math better if we wait until they have developed a foundation that will help them understand why it works.

In the meantime, there are ever so many interesting ideas we can explore together. Parents who think like mathematicians will always make time for the fun stuff.

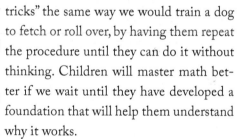

How many ways can you arrange one red, one yellow, and one blue bead on a string? When the order matters, you are counting permutations.

Mathematicians Ask Questions

Wise mathematicians are never satisfied with finding the answer to a problem. If they decide to put effort into solving any math puzzle, then they are determined to milk every drop of knowledge they can get from that problem. When mathematicians find an answer, they always go back and think about the problem again. Is there another way to look at it? Can we make our solution simpler or more elegant? Does this problem relate to any other mathematical idea? Can we expand our solution? Can we find a general principle?

As math teacher Herb Gross says, "What's really neat about mathematics is that even when there's only one right answer, there's never only one right way to do the problem."

School textbooks ask questions for which they know the answer. As we learn to think like mathematicians, we will ask a different type of question. Asking questions to which we don't know the answer can be frightening, because it forces us to give up the illusion of being in control. It makes us vulnerable, but it opens the door to learning.

- ♦ What do you think?

- ♦ What do you notice?

- ♦ What does it remind you of?

- ♦ What do you wonder?

- ♦ Is there another way to look at it?

- ♦ Will this always be true?

- ♦ If it's only true sometimes, what are the conditions that make it true? What conditions make it false?

- ♦ Could part of it be true and part of it be false?

- ♦ If this is false, then is something else true?

- ♦ Can you predict what will happen next?

- ♦ How did you figure that out?

- ♦ Is there a pattern?

- ♦ Will the pattern continue, or will it run out?

♦ How can we be sure?

♦ How would you change it?

♦ What would happen if ___?

♦ Why?

You can try asking your children questions to which you don't know the answer. Or encourage your kids to take the lead: "What questions can we ask about this?" When children learn to pose questions, that's when they start thinking like mathematicians.

As your children try to put their thoughts into words, keep in mind this truth:

> *Most remarks made by children consist of correct ideas very badly expressed. A good teacher will be wary of saying "No, that's wrong." Rather, he will try to discover the correct idea behind the inadequate expression. This is one of the most important principles in the whole of the art of teaching.*
>
> —W. W. Sawyer

Don't worry if you can't find the answers to all the questions you or your children ask. Some mathematical questions took centuries to answer and led to new branches of study, while others are still open. In the quest of learning math, wondering can be its own reward.

Mathematicians Love to Play

> *The mathematician plays a game in which he himself invents the rules while the physicist plays a game in which the rules are provided by nature, but as time goes on it becomes increasingly evident that the rules which the mathematician finds interesting are the same as those which nature has chosen.*
>
> — Paul Dirac

Mathematicians play with ideas. They toy with puzzles. They tinker with the connections between shapes and numbers, mystery and logic, growth and change. To a mathematician, the fun of the game is in experimenting, in trying new things and discovering what will happen. Many modern strategy games were invented for the puzzle of analyzing who would win.

For example, consider the simplest form of the two-player strategy game Nim. In this game, you start with a pile of pebbles or other small items. Take turns removing either one or two stones from the pile until one player is forced to take the last one, thus losing the game. Play the game with your children several times, and then encourage them to think of some way to change the rules. Ask questions: How does the game change? Is the new version easier or harder to win? Does the player who goes first have an advantage?

Parents who think like mathematicians will join their children in playing with numbers, shapes, and patterns. We might cut a sandwich in half, and then cut the halves in half, and then cut the half-halves in half, and see how small we can go. Or we may build a perfect square pyramid out of sugar cubes (with 1, 4, 9, 16, 25, 36, and 49 cubes in the layers) as the centerpiece for our next tea party.

Or we could think about new ideas: a point has no dimension, no length or width or size at all. But if we imagine pulling hard to stretch it out in one direction, it would become a one-dimensional line. A line pulled out and stretched into two dimensions becomes a square. A square

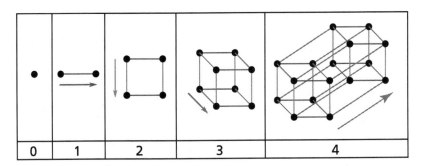

| 0 | 1 | 2 | 3 | 4 |

The dimension of an object is the number of ways a point can move on that object. On a line, for instance, a point can only move sideways, so a line is one-dimensional.
On a sheet of paper, however, a point could move sideways or up-and-down (or some combination of those two motions), so a flat shape is two-dimensional.
Because we live in a 3-D world, we can easily imagine shapes up to three dimensions, but higher dimensions seem strange and confusing. Some physicists speculate that the universe may have 10 or more dimensions, most of which are invisible to us.

stretched into three dimensions becomes a cube. So what would happen if we could stretch a cube into four dimensions?

Please don't be like the algebra teacher who caught a student playing tic-tac-toe and snatched away his paper, saying, "When you're in my classroom I expect you to work on mathematics." When the boy's friend, popular math writer Martin Gardner, heard the story, he responded that tic-tac-toe was an excellent introduction to symmetry, probability, set theory, multi-dimensional geometry, and other advanced topics. "With a little guidance," Gardner said, "it might have been much more rewarding than what his teacher was teaching."

Learning to think like a mathematician is a lifetime adventure. I don't have room in this book to mention perfect numbers, spherical geometry, Penrose tiles, cryptograms, or any of a zillion other topics waiting to be explored. When you begin to look at the world with a mathematician's eye, you embark on a journey more varied than the voyage of Ulysses. More exotic than Marco Polo's travels. More adventuresome than a trip to the moon.

A tangram sailboat for mathematical adventures.

When a kid is feeling bad
about being stuck with a problem,
or just very anxious,
I sometimes ask him
to make as many mistakes as he can
and as outrageous as he can.

Laughter happens
(which is valuable by itself,
and not only for the mood—
deep breathing brings oxygen to the brain).

Then the kid starts making mistakes.
In the process, features of the problem
become much clearer,
and in many cases
a way to a solution presents itself.

—MARIA DROUJKOVA

SECTION II

Playful Problem-Solving

The best way, it has always seemed to me, to make mathematics interesting to students and laymen is to approach it in a spirit of play.

—Martin Gardner

Math You Can Play

We can help children learn to read by filling their world with interesting words: riddles, read-aloud stories, letters from Grandma. We let them see us flipping through the newspaper, curling up in a chair with our ebook reader, or dragging stacks of books home from the library. This combination of example and environment promotes a lifelong love for reading.

Likewise, we can help our children learn to love mathematics by filling their world with intriguing ideas and math toys. Unschooling advocate Sandra Dodd recommends *strewing*, which means leaving colorful math books and interesting items scattered out around the house so that our kids might be tempted to pick them up and explore. What a wonderful idea!†

But environment is not enough. Before we can show our children how to play with math, we must recapture that "Aha!" feeling for ourselves. We have to forget the way we were taught. We must launch ourselves into the unknown. We adults need to learn how to play.

And when we find something interesting, our children will want to try it, too. "Hey, look what I found" is a fantastic motivator.

---

† *http://sandradodd.com/strewing*

Math That Is Social

My favorite playful math lessons rely on adult/child conversation, a proven method for increasing a child's reasoning skills. What better way could there be to do math than snuggling up on a couch with your little one, or standing side by side at the sink while your child helps you wash the dishes, or passing the time on a car ride into town?

"If you can read with your kids, then you can talk math with them," says Christopher Danielson, author of *Talking Math with Your Kids*. "You can support and encourage their developing mathematical minds. You don't need to love math. You don't need to have been particularly successful in school mathematics. You just need to notice when your children are being curious about math, and you need some ideas for turning that curiosity into a conversation."[†]

Math is a social activity—asking questions, posing puzzles, noticing connections, wondering "What if…?" All these things are easier for children to do in conversation with adults. Even the busiest families can find a few minutes here and there to talk about math. You can use everyday activities such as fixing snacks or grocery shopping to launch short chats about numbers, shapes, symmetry, or patterns.

In addition to such informal discussions, my kids and I have enjoyed social math in the form of oral story problems, mystery number puzzles, and the Today Game.

Tell Me a Story

As soon as your children can count past five, you can start giving them simple oral story problems to solve:

> *"If you have a cookie and I give you two more cookies, how many cookies will you have then?"*

The fastest way to a child's mind is through the taste buds. Children easily visualize their favorite foods, so I like to use edible stories at first. Then we expand our range, sharing stories about other familiar things: toys, pets, or trains.

---

† *http://talkingmathwithkids.com*

"Panther the barn cat went hunting in the field. He caught two mice every day. How many mice did he catch in four days?"

Don't limit your story problems to the child's grade level. If she can make a picture in her mind, she will be able to work with it. You may encourage your child to count on her fingers: one finger for each mouse. Using fingers as symbols is a step into abstraction, paving the way for later algebra. If you dislike finger-counting, then show your child how to use blocks or a rekenrek (next chapter, page 68) to work with bigger numbers than she can handle on her own.

"Panther went out to the woods and met a gray cat named Shadow. He invited her to come back to our barn and chase pigeons. There were fifteen pigeons in the barn. Panther chased six of them. He let Shadow have the rest. How many pigeons did Shadow chase?"

As you both get used to the game, you can occasionally throw in something harder, such as fractions, division with a remainder, or an answer that comes out negative. See what your child can do with a tough problem. You might be surprised: even a toddler has ideas about how to split three hot dogs between two people.

If your children are stumped, try not to give away the answer. Instead, ask them to explain the problem back to you. As children put a problem into their own words, they often see how to approach the solution. Pretend to be Socrates, asking questions to guide their thinking.

"After Shadow came to live in the barn, we had two cats, and half of them were girls. But then Shadow had four kittens. Now two-thirds of our barn cats are girls. How many of the kittens were girl cats?" [answer4]

Here is the most important rule of the oral story problem game: take turns. If I ask my daughter a story problem, she

Shadow, the tangram cat.
Tangram puzzles are explained
later in this chapter.

gets to give me one. And I have to try to solve it, even if she uses made-up numbers such as eighty-hundred or a gazillion. This is playtime, not an oral quiz.

Things to Consider in Creating Story Problems

- ♦ Some quantities are discrete and countable, such as marbles or dinosaurs. Other quantities are continuous, such as a pitcher of juice or a length of rope. We want our children to feel comfortable working with problems of both types.

- ♦ We often think of addition and subtraction as putting together or taking away sets of discrete items. But they can also be represented in stories by growth or comparison (how much more or less) or by classification (some are female cats and some are male).

- ♦ We often think of multiplication and division as counting or splitting up groups of items. But we can also think of these math processes as growth or shrinkage (how many times as much) or as rates and ratios (cookies per child, hot dogs per package).

- ♦ Division of continuous quantities may lead naturally to fractions (sharing pizza or candy bars).

- ♦ Money provides an excellent way for children to begin playing with decimal numbers.

If you have trouble coming up with stories, you can still make oral story

Equal sharing leads to fractions. Can you see how to divide this candy bar into halves, thirds, fourths, sixths, or twelfths?

problems a part of your routine by reading the blog Bedtime Math. Laura Overdeck posts a daily math story (with answers) at three levels of difficulty, preschool to middle-elementary.[†]

Oral story problems are not just for young children. Students of all ages benefit from the practice of working math in their heads. As your children grow, let the stories grow with them: soccer games, horse stories, or space adventures will keep older students figuring.

Can You Guess My Secret?

As they reach school age, children are ready to try a more abstract challenge. This doesn't mean you should stop playing with stories, but it's a good time to add another social math game to your repertoire. Now you can introduce the idea of variables, or unknown numbers.

Elementary textbooks slip a few pages of stealth algebra into even the earliest years with "missing addend" problems, which look like this: $5 + \underline{} = 7$. We call these mystery number problems, or sometimes we call them "What Number Am I?" (See page 13)

Encourage your children to do secret number problems, both orally and written out. My children love to do math with colored markers on a whiteboard. You can use a question mark or an empty square to stand for the mystery number.

And you can sometimes use a letter symbol, to ease your chil-

First grade algebra on a whiteboard. She solved my problems, and then she wrote some problems for me to solve. Like all artists, we signed our work.

---

† *http://bedtimemathproblem.org*

dren's transition to algebra: "I know a mystery number. I can't tell you its name, so I'll call it N. If you had N plus thirteen more, that would be twenty-five.

$$N + 13 = 25$$

"Can you tell what my secret number is?"

Don't forget to take turns. When you let the kids make up problems for you, math remains a game. Children love trying to outwit adults.

Social Number Games

If you pay attention to the everyday numbers around you, you will see plenty of opportunities to play with mental math. Try posting a small whiteboard on the front of your refrigerator with "Today is [Month] [Date]" written across the top. Throughout the day, family members can write different creative names for the date. For instance, I am typing this on November 14, so we might invent such names as:

$$1 + 2 + 3 + 2 + 1 + 2 + 3$$
$$4 \times 7 \div 2$$
$$20 - (10 - 4)$$
$$56 \times \tfrac{1}{4}$$
$$84 - 70$$

Or watch the display on your digital clock. How many number expressions or math equations can you make with the time?

$$8{:}24 \text{ makes } 8 = 2 \times 4$$
$$10{:}43 \text{ makes } 1 + 0 = 4 - 3$$
$$1{:}03 \text{ is the prime number } 103 = \text{prime time}$$

Keep a chart, and let family members add a sticker for each "clock math" expression they find. Whoever wins the most stickers is proclaimed the family's Clock Math Champion.

Math That Is Beautiful

Many mathematicians have claimed that math is beautiful. For instance:

*The mathematician does not study pure mathematics because it is useful;
he studies it because he delights in it and he delights in it because it is
beautiful.*

—JULES HENRI POINCARÉ

*A mathematician, like a painter or poet, is a maker of patterns. If his
patterns are more permanent than theirs, it is because they are made
with ideas. The mathematician's patterns, like the painter's or the poet's
must be beautiful; the ideas, like the colors or the words must fit together
in a harmonious way. Beauty is the first test: there is no permanent
place in this world for ugly mathematics.*

—G. H. HARDY

*Mathematics, rightly viewed, possesses not only truth, but supreme
beauty—a beauty cold and austere, like that of sculpture, without appeal
to any part of our weaker nature, without the gorgeous trappings of
painting or music, yet sublimely pure, and capable of a stern perfection
such as only the greatest art can show.*

—BERTRAND RUSSELL

*Why are numbers beautiful? It's like asking why is Beethoven's Ninth
Symphony beautiful. If you don't see why, someone can't tell you. I know
numbers are beautiful. If they aren't beautiful, nothing is.*

—PAUL ERDŐS

For most of history, it took a trained mind to appreciate this beauty. Most
people didn't see it at all. They probably assumed that long years of study
had addled the mathematicians' brains. Now, modern computer graphics
let everyone see a little of the glory in math, and you can share it with your
children by doing a web search for "fractal art."

When mathematicians talk about the beauty of math, however, they
don't mean the swirling colors of a fractal zoom video. Rather, they have
in mind a particularly satisfying or insightful proof. Logic can lead to surprising results or establish deep connections between concepts that at first
glance seem unrelated. Visual proofs like the penny square in Chapter 1
(page 11) (that adding the first n odd numbers creates n^2) delight us
by demonstrating mathematical truth without words. Unexpected results
such as the following puzzle fill us with wonder:

- Draw a *quadrilateral*—a shape with four straight sides that connect all the way around. Make it neat and orderly like a square. Or wild and lopsided like my shapes below.

- Measure with a ruler, and put a dot at the center (*midpoint*) of each side.

- Connect the dots to make another four-sided shape.

- What do you notice?

- Does it make you curious?

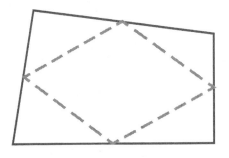 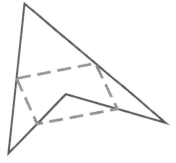

Draw a four-sided shape. Connect the midpoints of each side.
How is your new shape different from the original one?

No matter how crazy your original four-sided shape, connecting the midpoints will always produce a nicely symmetrical *parallelogram*—the sides opposite each other are exactly alike. It's almost as if the shapes are conspiring to bring order out of quadrilateral chaos.

Paul Lockhart shared this puzzle in the trailer video for his book *Measurement*. "I would have expected: you make some crazy blob and connect the middles, it's gonna be another crazy blob. But it isn't—it's always a slanted box, beautifully parallel," he says. "The mathematical question is *why?* It's always why. And the only way we know how to answer such questions is to come up, from scratch, with these narrative arguments—these elegant reason-poems [called proofs]—that explain it."[†]

Your children may be too young to see the splendor of logical elegance in a mathematical proof, but they can still relish the beauty of math in geometric designs.

---

† *https://youtu.be/V1gT2f3Fe44*

Pattern Blocks and Tangrams

Most preschool and elementary-age children will enjoy pattern blocks: colorful, flat, plastic or wooden blocks in an assortment of shapes. Pattern blocks give the challenge of quilt design without the rigor of stitching pieces. In educational jargon, they help children investigate geometric forms and relationships while exploring symmetry, congruence, and angle measurement.

You will want a big set so more than one person can play. Try some of these ideas:

- ♦ Sort the blocks, or stack them, or build with them.

- ♦ Make row patterns (such as: red, blue, blue, red, blue …), also known as "What comes next?"

- ♦ Make area (filled-in) patterns, covering the table like a quilt.

- ♦ Take turns adding blocks to make a design.

- ♦ Try to duplicate each other's creations. For older children, make this more challenging by sitting back-to-back on the floor while one person tries to describe his design so the other can build a copy.

- ♦ Make symmetric and asymmetric patterns. Which do you prefer?

- ♦ How many red pieces (trapezoids) does it take to make the same shape as a yellow piece (hexagon)?

- ♦ How many different ways can you make the hexagon shape?

Pattern blocks come in six basic shapes with matching
sides, so they fit together in any arrangement.

Talk about your designs as you work, but avoid turning the session into a lecture about fractions.

As children grow, they will begin to appreciate ideas that are more abstract. Starting in second or third grade, you can introduce your kids to tangrams: seven geometric shapes that fit together to form a square, sailboat, house, goldfish, knight fighting a dragon, or a child reading a book.

Tangrams are an old Chinese puzzle, though perhaps not as ancient as some books would lead you to believe. (Sam Loyd wrote his book of tangram puzzles, *The Eighth Book of Tan*, in 1903. He invented a 4,000-year history that some authors have mistaken for fact.) Like many Chinese art forms, tangrams are simple yet elegant. Read together Ann Tompert's delightful book, *Grandfather Tang's Story*, or the Scholastic Reader *Three Pigs, One Wolf, Seven Magic Shapes* by Grace Maccarone. My young children loved the Learning Resources workbook *Tangrammables*. Older students and adults will enjoy the game Tangoes. A number of online sites offer tangram puzzles as well.

Engrossed in pattern blocks or tangrams, children soak up math principles without realizing it—the relationships between parallel and perpendicular lines, similar triangles, acute and obtuse angles. They improve their visualization skills. They build a subconscious foundation for later geometry: Why is the area of a triangle half that of a rectangle? Why is the area of a parallelogram related to its height and not the length of its slanted side? You could buy workbooks that make all this explicit, but I would rather let the kids play. Worksheet exercises are a chore to finish, soon forgotten, but the relationships and connections that children discover on their own belong to them forever.

How to Make Tangrams

On graph paper, enlarge the following pattern to a comfortable size. Trace and cut from cardboard or craft foam. Make each set a different color, so you can tell at a glance if you have all the pieces.

You can put self-sticking magnetic strips on the back of each piece for refrigerator tangrams, or slip a set in your bag as a quiet toy for restaurants or waiting rooms.

Hundreds of pictures can be created with these simple puzzle pieces,

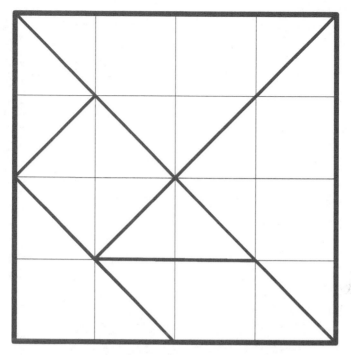

Tangram pattern. How many fractions of
the original square can you see?

When you are trying to solve a tangram puzzle, you
may have to flip the parallelogram piece over. The
two sides are mirror images of each other.

including every letter of the alphabet. Can your child make his initials? Or start with this cuddly kitten. You will find other tangram puzzles throughout this book, including the numbers for each chapter.

Create Your Own Tangram Puzzles

Your children can make up their own pictures, too. They might use the square for a head, perhaps with triangle ears like the kitten, and then mix the other pieces around until they shape a satisfying body. Or start with a large triangle sail and create a boat.

Abstract shapes are easier for beginners to invent. And they are often harder to solve, much to the child's delight. Suppose my daughter came up with this abstract glob:

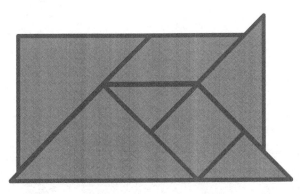

Now she wants to make a puzzle to challenge her dad or me. First, she gets a plain sheet of paper and lays out her design on that. Then she holds the pieces down with one hand while she traces around the outline. Finally, she removes the tangram pieces.

Ta-da! A tangram stumper.

Museum-Quality Math

While you are doing math art, you may also want to experiment with origami geometry. If you don't have origami paper, cut colorful squares from magazine ads or gift wrapping paper. If your children are in 4-H, they can enter their origami creations in the county fair.[†]

Or you might play with *tessellations:* repeating patterns that fit together with no gaps, like checker board squares or quilt pieces. This is the hobby that made M. C. Escher famous, with his amazing drawings of nestled salamanders, dancing fish, black geese flying through a flock of white geese, armored knights on horseback, and many more.[‡]

Children will enjoy using the Roylco Tessellations Animal Templates to make their own designs. For those who want to create original patterns, provide a ruler, tracing paper, and enough time for the kids to lose themselves in the puzzle. Check your library for *The Adventures of Penrose the Mathematical Cat* by Theoni Pappas, which has a section on tessellating shapes.

Tessellating patterns—such as this arrangement of pattern blocks—
fill a flat space and can be imagined as repeating to infinity.

---

† *http://www.ics.uci.edu/~eppstein/junkyard/origami.html*
‡ *http://www.mathsisfun.com/geometry/tessellation.html*

Math That Is Fun

Your children may rebel over a page of arithmetic practice, but most kids love to play games. Therefore, whenever possible, turn math into a game. Math games come in two flavors: drill and strategy. Drill games let children practice things they have studied in math, such as addition or multiplication facts. Strategy games relate less directly to math class but provide a chance to develop logical thinking skills.

Drill Games

To play math drill games, make a deck of math cards by removing the jokers and face cards from a normal deck of poker or bridge style playing cards. This will give you a forty-card stack containing four sets of ace (one) to ten.

After children begin to learn addition, they can practice simple sums with Tens Fish. This game is Go Fish with a twist, collecting tens and pairs that make ten. If you have a six, for instance, you would fish for a four to match it.

As their arithmetic skills improve, many kids enjoy Math War. Each player puts down two cards. Whoever has the largest sum (or difference or product, depending on which math facts you want to work on) takes that trick.

Middle school or older children can play Twenty-Four. Deal four cards to each player. Try to be the first person to use all your cards in a multistep equation that makes the target number 24. You can add, subtract, multiply, or divide, but use each card only once. For example, a hand of 4, 3, 7, and 9 could make:

$$(9 \times 3) - 7 + 4 = 24$$

or

$$(9 - 7) \times 3 \times 4 = 24$$

but not

$$(9 - 3) \times 4 = 24,$$

which ignores the 7 card.

This game has an element of luck. Some hands will not make twenty-four no matter how you combine them. If nobody can make an equation, discard that hand and try again.

You can keep score, if you like. Whoever makes the first valid equation wins that hand and scores one point. After the first player makes an equation, the rest lay down their cards. Help each other, offering advice until everyone either gets an equation or decides his hand is impossible. Pass the deal to the left. The player who scores five points wins the game.

Strategy Games

The childhood strategy game tic-tac-toe is boring once you know the trick. After your children master the basic game, however, you can tweak the strategy by letting the game board grow. Either player may extend the original lines or add new ones to the edge of the game board to create new squares as needed. (Or play on graph paper, if you'd rather not draw all those lines.) Three in a row will be too easy, so a player must get five in a row to win. This is Gomoku, an international classic.

Strategy games develop reasoning skills. They help break through the "I can't do it" feeling of math anxiety, which makes them good medicine when you need to revive a mathematically discouraged child. One excellent game for players of all ages, combining logical strategy with visual perception, is the card game Set.[†]

Library books can bring you folk games from around the world, many of which are excellent strategy challenges. And while most families enjoy the classic board games, such as chess or checkers, many have never heard of newer delights like Quarto.[‡] Search your favorite online toy or

---

† *http://www.setgame.com*
‡ *http://quarto.mygamesonline.org/en*

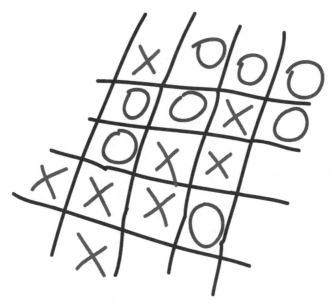

A game of Gomoku. You are playing X, and it's your turn. So far, O has blocked your every move. What will you try next?

school-supply store for modern strategy board games. They make wonderful gifts.

You can also find instructions for several drill and strategy games at my blog, or look for my *Math You Can Play* series at your favorite online bookseller.[†]

If you introduce one or two new games per month, that will allow time for your children to practice and internalize the rules. It won't be long until the kids are picking up the games and playing on their own. With any luck, you will never hear "There's nothing to do!" again.

---

†   *http://denisegaskins.com/category/all–about–math/activities/games*
    http://tabletopacademy.net/playful–math–books/math–you–can–play

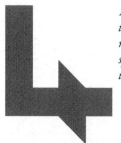

It is not enough for a child to hear an idea explained, and to understand it. If that is all we do, the idea may leave no trace in the child's memory at all. Children need to spend time with the idea, to play around with it, to use it themselves.

—W. W. SAWYER

Math You Can Touch

MANY ADULTS REMEMBER OUR OWN struggles with math and hope to provide a better experience for the next generation. We know that young children often learn by getting their whole bodies involved, by touching and holding and moving things around as they explore new ideas. It makes sense, therefore, that we should balance abstract instruction with hands-on demonstrations. Geoboards, plastic teddy bears, fraction circles … school-supply vendors offer a bewildering variety of *manipulatives,* which are special toys designed to help children learn math.

With my first child, I thought we needed something special, a sort of "magic bullet" for math. I bought a cute set of colorful Cuisenaire rods with a poster and task cards.

"Line up the rods in order by color," said Task Card #1. "Notice the stair-step pattern."

My son, then age seven, wanted to build towers.

"No, look," I said. "We're supposed to find all the combinations of different rods that make the same length as the orange."

The boy would work with the rods when I forced him to, going through the motions with little enthusiasm. Then he'd spend hours building a complicated structure with his Lego blocks. Legos offered a greater variety of size and shape relationships than the math rods. They helped

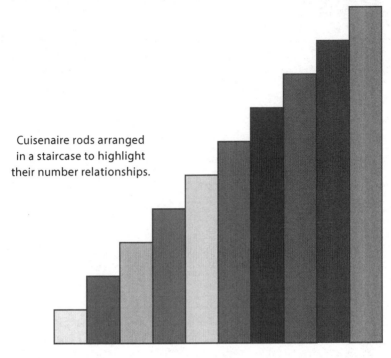

Cuisenaire rods arranged in a staircase to highlight their number relationships.

develop his visual perception skills in three dimensions, while the rods focused primarily on the single dimension of length. Besides geometry, my son was learning about sorting and classification, the beginnings of science. He gained hands-on experience with statistics and probability. (What were the chances of finding the right block with a random grab?) He worked intuitively with combinations and permutations, with symmetric and asymmetric designs. And he occasionally counted the blocks.

If I had realized sooner that normal toys could be such valuable math manipulatives, I might have saved my money.

In the end, however, I'm glad I bought the Cuisenaire rods. By the time my youngest child came around, I had worked my way through the elementary curriculum several times. In the process I learned to appreciate what a versatile math tool the rods are—a tool that can help children understand ideas from counting and simple addition to fractions and ratios.

Besides, they do make nice towers.

What Makes a Manipulative?

Properly used, manipulatives help make concrete such abstract concepts as *number, angle, area,* and *perimeter.* They empower our children to live the dream envisioned by mathematical philosopher Alfred North White-head: "From the very beginning of his education, the child should experience the joy of discovery."

Manipulatives act as a physical metaphor for a mathematical relationship: that five of *this* are the same amount as one of *that.* At first, we think of the small, white block as one. So the "five this per that" relationship makes the longer, yellow block represent five. But as our children learn to work with large numbers, the shorter block may represent any amount. The longer block will still be five times as much. And when we move into fractions, we can go the other way. Let the long block represent one whole thing. How much is the shorter block worth?

Have you ever wondered why children count on their fingers? These natural counting tools are built right into our bodies. We experience them every day in a thousand unstructured situations. We are intimately familiar with our fingers, so we can use them to help us think through a

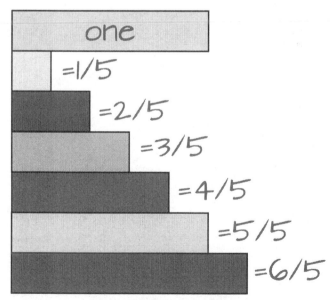

If the yellow block is one whole unit, then each of the other blocks represents some fractional part of that unit.

problem. In the same way, I encourage you to give your children freedom to play with math toys: wooden blocks, Legos, Cuisenaire rods, whatever they might have. Through the experience of unstructured play, children gain the familiarity that leads to understanding. This is what I failed to recognize when I tried to force my son to follow those task cards. After extended play—when the manipulatives begin to seem as natural as fingers—your children will then be ready to use them to make sense of abstract mathematical ideas.

But remember that there's no magic in manipulatives. Blocks can help children see and work with ideas that are already in their minds, but physical models alone cannot communicate abstract concepts. The hands-on exploration provides specific experiences, but we want to develop general understanding. For that, children need to put their own thoughts into words and compare them with the thoughts of other minds through conversation.

For example, we could turn that "make the same length as the orange" idea from my Cuisenaire rod task cards into a game that could spark all sorts of discussion, like this:

- ♦ The first player chooses any rod (yellow or longer) and sets it in the middle of the table.

- ♦ Then players alternate adding a new row of two or more rods that make the same length.

- ♦ Each row must be different from all those already played.

- ♦ Whoever plays the last legal row, leaving his opponent stumped, wins that round and gets to choose a new starting rod.

Depending on the age of your child, you may want to keep "score" by writing an expression to represent each row. Writing everything out does not increase the mathematical content of the game. The written symbols are not mathematics, any more than the lines and dots written on a staff are music. Music only happens when we play the notes, just as math only happens when we think the ideas. Your children will be thinking like a mathematician, even if they write nothing down. But writing the equations can help them learn arithmetic notation, which will be useful when they want to communicate their mathematical thoughts.

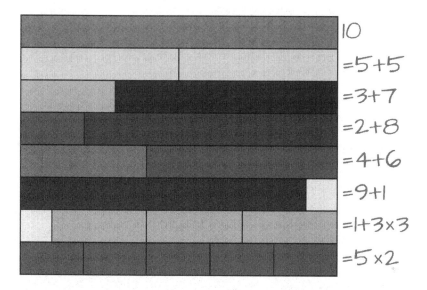

10
=5+5
=3+7
=2+8
=4+6
=9+1
=1+3×3
=5×2

A Cuisenaire rod game in progress. Can you make a new row?

I love Rosie's version of this game at her Education Unboxed website: "Having a Party." All the party guests need to bring enough friends to match the length of their host, the original block. "Six is having a party, and One wants to come, so she has to bring her friend Five…"[†]

Homespun Math Manipulatives

My children's first math manipulative was a grilled cheese sandwich. "Do you want yours cut in halves or fourths? Would you prefer triangles or rectangles?"

If you're on a tight budget, try making your own math manipulatives from craft supplies or garage sale finds. A big box of craft popsicle sticks and some rubber bands will give your children hours of number play. Count the sticks, bundle them in sets of ten, bundle ten tens together to make a hundred. Add numbers and subtract them, creating or unwrapping bundles as needed to show how our place-value system works. (*Place value* means that a 4 in the tens place is not worth the same amount as a 4 in the ones place.) Use craft sticks to act out story problems. Build

---

† *http://www.educationunboxed.com/having-a-party*

stick patterns. Use the sticks as a measuring unit: how many sticks tall are you? Lie on the floor and find out.

A large jar of assorted coins makes a wonderful math toy. Children love to play with, count, and sort coins. Add a dollar bill to the jar, so you can play the Dollar Game: Take turns throwing a pair of dice, gathering that many pennies and trading up to bigger coins. Five pennies trade for a nickel, two nickels for a dime, etc. Whoever is the first to claim the dollar wins the game.

Or take the Penny Birthday Challenge to learn about exponential growth: Print out a calendar for your child's birthday month. Put one penny on the first day of the month, two pennies on the second day, four pennies on the third day, etc. If you continued doubling the pennies each day until you reach your child's birthday, how much money would you need? (Warning: do not promise to give the money to your child unless the birthday comes near the beginning of the month.)

And add to your math repertoire the following three homemade tools that will help your children develop a rich understanding of numbers: a rekenrek, a number line, and a hundred chart.

Beware the Penny Birthday Challenge! Those pennies will add up to dollars much faster than most people expect.

Counting by Fives and Tens

In order to move from simple counting to logic-based arithmetic, children need to internalize the link between our bodies and our number system. We have five fingers on each hand. To count six is one hand plus one more. Seven is a five and two more. Eight is five and three more. Nine is five and four. Two hands have ten fingers in all, which is why we organize our numbers in groups of tens and ten-tens (hundreds). Because five and

An early 19th century school abacus.

ten are fundamental to our number system, we need to give our children many opportunities to experience these numbers in different ways.

A rekenrek is a two-row version of a school abacus or counting frame. Unlike a traditional abacus, where each row represents a new place-value column, the beads on a counting frame are all worth the same amount: one. The alternating colors help children relate numbers to the fundamental counting groups of five and ten.

You can buy a rekenrek, but it's easy to make your own. For each rekenrek, you will need:

- two chenille stems (craft pipe cleaners) or two 16-inch lengths of cord (the elastic type works well)
- twenty pony beads (ten each in two colors)
- 3 × 6 inch (7.5 × 15 cm) rectangle of craft foam

Many people use red and white beads, to match the commercial version, but feel free to choose any colors your children like—the important thing is to have two distinct colors, grouped by fives. One standard sheet of colorful craft foam can make up to a dozen rekenreks. Cardboard would also work for the backing, but it's not nearly as pretty.

- ♦ Cut four half-inch slits on the short edges of your craft foam rectangle: two on each end, spaced as evenly as you can. If you are using cord, make the slits only a quarter-inch deep.

- ♦ Load ten beads on each chenille stem (or each cord): five of one color, then five of the other. Push the beads to the center.

- ♦ Lay the stems out parallel to the long side of the rectangle, making sure the colors are in the same order on both.

- ♦ Fit the wires (or stretch the cord) snugly into the slits. Fold the extra lengths to the back, but not so tightly that the craft foam warps.

- ♦ Twist the stems together in the back, or tie knots in the elastic cords. Fold the ends down to cover the pointy wire tips of the chenille stems, or wrap duct tape around to keep the tips from snagging on clothes and fingers.

Now you are ready to play. Let your child count the beads or slide them into groups. The alternating colors encourage children to recognize number relationships. "Eight" is no longer just a bunch of individual pieces. It's also "five and three more" and "two less than ten."

How many different ways can the beads go into groups? All ten beads at one end, or two groups of five, or five pairs, or a three and a seven, or … what else? Or you might slide some of the beads to one end, covering them with your hand: "How many beads are hiding?" Ask your child to

As children work with the rekenrek beads, they learn to visualize numbers in a way that leads to mental math skills. See several examples in Chapter 8 (page 148).

make a hidden-beads puzzle for you to solve.

The Math Learning Center offers a free PDF booklet with activity and game ideas: *Using the Rekenrek as a Visual Model for Strategic Reasoning in Mathematics* by Barbara Blanke.[†]

Number Line

With a whimsical number line, negative numbers are easy for children to understand. To start this process, get a sheet of poster board. Paint a tree with roots or perhaps a boat on the ocean, with water and fish below and bright sky above. Use big brushes, so you are not tempted to put in too much detail. A wide permanent marker works well to draw in your number line, with zero at ground (or sea) level and the negative numbers down below. Finally, spray with fixative or cover with contact paper to keep the poster paint from smearing on little fingers.

Hang the number line on your wall. Then tell each other story problems while you run your fingers up for the positive numbers and down for the negatives to count out your answers.

> *"I climbed up three meters into the tree, but then I decided I'd rather dig a hole to China. I went down a total of five meters from my lofty perch. How deep was my hole?"*

Written as a math equation, that story looks like this: $(+3) + (-5) = -2$.

> *"Dad thought he could dig a better hole than mine. He dug down one meter. Then he dug down two more meters. Then he dug three more after that. How deep did he go?"*

That would be: $(-1) + (-2) + (-3) = -6$.

> *"A squirrel went into Dad's hole looking for nuts. Then the dog ran outside to bark at him, so he scrambled up the tree as fast as he could go. From the bottom of the hole, the squirrel climbed ten meters. Did he make it safely out of Fido's reach?"*

This time: $(-6) + (+10) = +4$.

---

† *http://catalog.mathlearningcenter.org/store/product-8473.htm*
http://www.mathlearningcenter.org/web-apps/number-rack

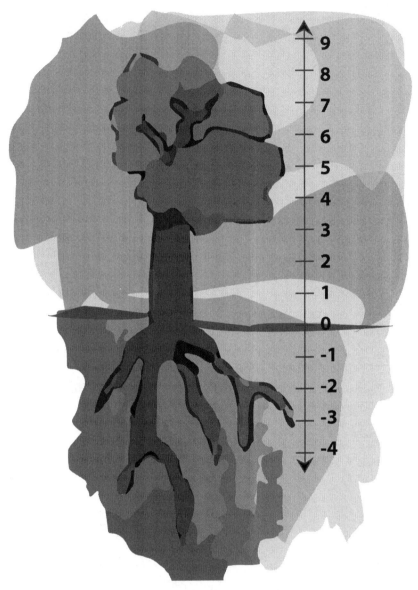

Young children can develop intuition about negative
numbers by counting up and down on a number line.
Older kids can expand their understanding of subtraction
to include "finding the distance between two points."

Or put the number line at a slant, like a hill on which you can run up and down. In many applications of math and physics, "zero" is an arbitrary location, based on whatever makes our problem easy to solve. In this case, you might invent a peasant who lives in a small hut at zero, partway up the hill, and dreams of becoming a knight. At the top of the hill is a castle, and at the bottom there is a cave where a terrible dragon lives. Take turns making up story problem adventures.

Negative numbers can be fun. And, despite that second grade teacher who told us we couldn't subtract six from four, negative numbers help clarify many real-life situations: winter temperatures, for example, or the bank account of someone who relies too much on credit cards.

A Line Without Numbers

As your children advance in elementary arithmetic, they will outgrow the need to count every answer. Introduce older students to the open number line, a powerful tool for keeping track of mental arithmetic.

Sketch a straight, unmarked line on a whiteboard or scratch paper. Where are the numbers? They're wherever we need them to be. We write the numbers in as we work through the problem. Suppose we want to calculate the following problem:

$$337 - 158 = ?$$

We can use an open number line to keep track where we are in each step, like this:

- ♦ Draw a straight line on the whiteboard or paper. This line can go any direction: vertical, horizontal, or slantwise. I'll use a vertical line for this example.

- ♦ Start with the first number. I'll mark 337 near the top of my line, since I'm going to subtract.

- ♦ Mark new numbers in whatever way helps you think about the problem. I'll jump down 100, landing at 237.

- ♦ Now I have 58 left to take away. It's easy to take 30 more, which lands me at 207.

- ◆ I still need to take away 28 to get my answer. I'll take another 30, since that's easier: twenty tens take away three tens. That brings me down to 177.

- ◆ And since I took away too much, I need to go back up two spaces. My final answer is 179.

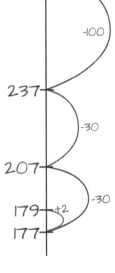

Don't worry about drawing the jumps on an open number line to scale. It is a thinking tool, not an exercise in precision drafting.

If you do buddy math (see Chapter 8, page 144), you can use open number lines to explain how you think through your answers. Your children will follow your lead. Visualizing numbers in this way will strengthen their growing math skills.

Hundred Chart

The hundred chart (also called a hundred board) is a ten by ten square grid with the natural numbers 1–100, like a number line that has been cut up and laid in rows. Some people prefer to use the whole numbers 0–99, which keeps the single-digit numbers and the numbers in each decade on the same row.

Your child can help you make a hundred chart on a sheet of construction paper or poster board. Make the squares big enough that you can mark them with pennies, blocks, or toy dinosaurs. Or download and print Yelena McManaman's hundred chart poster for your wall.[†]

Hundred Chart Counting Patterns

Use the chart to look for counting patterns. Patterns are interesting, and they prepare children for multiplication and for algebra.

- ◆ Count up.

- ◆ Count down.

---

† *www.MoebiusNoodles.com/2013/01/The-Hundred-Chart-And-Game-Cards*

Vocabulary

The positive numbers beginning at one are called the *natural numbers* because they are the ones that children naturally count with. When zero is included, we call them the *whole numbers*. The *integers* include the natural numbers, zero, and the negative whole numbers, too. Zero is neither positive nor negative—it acts like a boundary wall between the two.

All of these sets are important in mathematics. And don't forget the numbers between the numbers! A number line can help students understand fractions and decimals, too.

By the way, there is no clear consensus among mathematicians on whether to include zero among the natural numbers. Computer programmers often begin counting with zero. If you've heard different definitions for the terms *natural* and *whole* numbers, use them as you prefer. But when you come to a math problem where it matters, say something more precise, such as "the non-negative integers including [or excluding] zero."

♦ Use the hundred chart as a number line to do addition and subtraction with numbers up to one hundred. Take turns making up problems for each other to solve. Build mental math skills by showing how to add or subtract the tens first (counting up or down) then the ones (counting left or right).

♦ Skip count by twos or threes or tens, starting at any number. Begin by whisper counting: *one, two,* THREE, *four, five,* SIX ... Remember to take turns. If you tell your daughter to count by fives, she gets to make you do elevens.

♦ Or mark all the numbers with seven in them. Why do they make that pattern? What other patterns can you find?

♦ Look for addition or subtraction patterns. 3 + 9 = ? Now go to 23 + 9, 33 + 9, 63 + 9. What do you notice? What do 15 − 7, 25 − 7, and 45 − 7 have in common? Find other patterns.

1	2	3	4	5	6	7	8	9	10
11	12	13	14	15	16	17	18	19	20
21	22	23	24	25	26	27	28	29	30
31	32	33	34	35	36	37	38	39	40
41	42	43	44	45	46	47	48	49	50
51	52	53	54	55	56	57	58	59	60
61	62	63	64	65	66	67	68	69	70
71	72	73	74	75	76	77	78	79	80
81	82	83	84	85	86	87	88	89	90
91	92	93	94	95	96	97	98	99	100

A traditional hundred chart counts down from the top of the page, like reading a book. Some children find it more intuitive to use a chart that counts up, with the higher-value numbers at the top. You can download free printables of both styles from my website.
http://tabletopacademy.net/playful-math-books/free-printables

Hundred Chart Puzzles and Games

Many of the following activities require printing out a hundred chart. You can use the printables I mentioned above or try Scott Bryce's Math Worksheet Site, which allows you to choose whether you want the numbers 1–100 or 0–99.[†]

♦ Play the Nickel Game: Give each player twenty nickels or other small tokens. One player thinks of a secret number. The second player makes a guess by placing a nickel on a number. The first player points up (if the guess is too low) or down (if the guess is too high). The second player continues to pay out nickels until the secret number is revealed. The first player collects all the

---

† *http://themathworksheetsite.com/h_chart.html*

nickels on the board. Then the second player picks a number for the first one to guess.

♦ Make picture puzzles. You give the clues, either a description of a number ("It's two less than twenty-six") or an equation that equals that number. Your child solves the equation and colors in the appropriate square. Repeat to make a design. Now, let your child make up a puzzle for you to color.

♦ Cut up a hundred board into six or more irregular pieces, cutting along the lines (not row by row) to make a "jigsaw" puzzle. For more of a challenge, cut a blank chart into six or more irregular puzzle pieces, writing in one or two numbers per piece. Can your child put the chart back together and fill in the rest of the numbers?

1	2	3	4	5	6	7	8	9	10
11	12	13	14	15	16	17	18	19	20
21	22	23	24	25	26	27	28	29	30
31	32	33	34	35	36	37	38	39	40
41	42	43	44	45	46	47	48	49	50
51	52	53	54	55	56	57	58	59	60
61	62	63	64	65	66	67	68	69	70
71	72	73	74	75	76	77	78	79	80
81	82	83	84	85	86	87	88	89	90
91	92	93	94	95	96	97	98	99	100

A hundred chart heart picture. Give a clue for each number: "Color ten more than sixty-three. The double of thirty. The number that's half of seventy…"

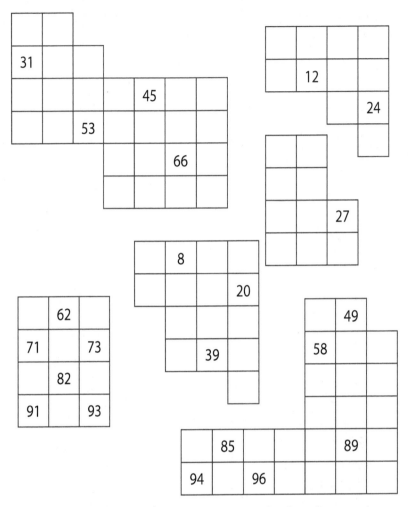

- Make arrow codes. On your paper or whiteboard, write the starting number and several arrows. Each arrow means to move one square in the direction indicated. What number is "45 ← ← ↑ → ↑"? How would you use arrows to write, "Start at twenty-seven and move to fifty-nine"?

- Play Race to 100: Take turns rolling a pair of dice. Move that many spaces on the hundred chart. If you predict your landing place before you move (without counting squares), then you can go one extra space as a bonus. The first person to reach or pass 100 wins the game.

- A cross pattern is a square plus the four squares up, down, left, and right from it. An X pattern is a square plus the four touching it diagonally. Choose any square that is not on an edge of the hundred board. Find its cross and X patterns. Add up their sums. Can you explain why they add up to the same number? Find other patterns that work that way. [Hint: Think about symmetry.] Can you predict the cross or X pattern sum for any number? Find the cross and X patterns for a date on this month's calendar. How are these like the patterns on a hundred board? How are they different?

- Try Terry Kawas's Hundred Board Logic puzzles. Then make up similar puzzles of your own.†

Hundred Chart Ideas for Older Students

- Count by whatever number you want, but start at an unusual place. Count by two, but start with thirty-seven. Or count by five, starting at eighteen. Or for a tougher challenge, practice your mental subtraction skills: count down by the number of your choice.

- How many numbers are there from eleven to twenty-five? Are you sure? What does it mean to count from one number to another? Does it include the first number, or the last one, or both, or neither? Talk about inclusive and exclusive counting. Then make up counting puzzles for each other.

- Play Gomoku. Use a wide-tip marker to make X's and O's, or use pennies and nickels to mark the squares. On each turn, you must make up a calculation that equals the number in the square you want to mark. Five in a row wins the game.

- Look for multiplication patterns. Colored bingo disks are good for this, or use pinto beans. Mark the numbers you hit when you count by twos. What pattern do they make? Make the counting-by-three pattern, or mark the sevens, etc. Why does

---

† http://www.mathwire.com/problemsolving/hblogic.html

the counting-by-five pattern go down the way it does? Why do the nines move slantwise across the chart?

- ♦ Mark the multiplication patterns by putting colored dots along one edge or corner of each square. (For instance, all the multiples of two get a red dot, the multiples of three get green dots, etc.) Which numbers have the most dots? Which numbers have just one dot? Which don't have any?

- ♦ Make the Sieve of Eratosthenes, named after the ancient Greek librarian who invented this method for finding prime numbers. On a printed chart, blacken the box for the number one, which is neither prime nor composite. Circle the next unmarked number, two, and then cross out all of its multiples. That is, count by twos and cross out every number you land on, except for two itself. Circle the next unmarked number, three, and then cross out all of its multiples. Keep going until every number is either circled (prime) or crossed out (composite).

The hundred chart can also help your children convert between fractions, decimals, and percents:

- ♦ What number is half of 100? Can you use the chart to show why that's true? What number is three-fourths of 100? How can you prove it?

- ♦ What other fractions of 100 can you find? One-tenth? Two-fifths?

- ♦ Can you find a number that is one-third of 100?

- ♦ *Percent* means "out of 100." So 30% means "thirty out of 100," which is how much of the whole chart?

- ♦ If we say that the chart is one whole unit, then how much is each row (in decimal notation)? What size is each box?

- ♦ Can you color 0.47 of the chart?

- ♦ What decimal would mean the same as one-fifth of the chart? What percent of the chart would that be?

The ancient Greek scientist Eratosthenes was the first person to accurately calculate the earth's circumference. In 236 BC, he became the chief librarian of the Great Library of Alexandria, the capital of Ptolemaic Egypt. In math, we remember Eratosthenes for his sieve, which is not a strainer for noodles and veggies, but a quick way to filter out the primes from a list of numbers arranged in increasing order.

More Hands-On Fun

Encourage your children to measure everything. Put cups and measuring spoons in the bathtub or sandbox, or give them a big tub of rice to scoop up. Find a yardstick, or let them use a tape measure. Run races or make an obstacle course, keeping time with a stopwatch. And kids love to help with cooking. What could be tastier "homework" than a double batch of chocolate chip cookies?

You can measure the rooms in your house. Draw floor plans on graph paper. Measure each piece of furniture and cut out scale models. How many different ways could you arrange the furniture? Plan a new layout for your bedroom.

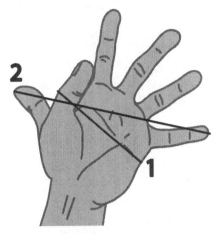

Classic measurement:
(1) a hand, (2) a span.

Or try measuring things the old-fashioned way, with hands, spans, cubits, and paces. A *hand* is the distance across the palm and thumb, or about the size of a closed fist. A *span* is the widest part of spread-out fingers. A *cubit* is the length from elbow to fingertips. A *pace* is a large step from heel to heel. How long are these in inches or centimeters?

This could lead to a discussion of standards. Ask younger children, "If you were buying a yard of cloth, measured from fingertips to nose, who would you rather have measure it: Grandma or your little sister?"

Older children can investigate the *Constitution of the United States*, Article 1, Section 8.5: "Congress shall have Power to ... fix the Standard of Weights and Measures." Why did our founding fathers write that?

Take Up Drafting

You will want to keep graph paper on hand for drawing, designing, and making patterns. Many of the pattern block investigations from Chapter 3 (page 55) may be done on graph paper:

♦ Make a pattern of colored squares in a row, also known as "What comes next?"

♦ Make area patterns, like quilt squares. Draw diagonal lines if you want triangular sections for your pattern.

♦ Make a pattern that grows according to your secret rule. What is the pattern's first stage? Second stage? Third stage? Can you predict what would be the 10th stage, or the 100th?

♦ Try to duplicate each other's patterns. For older students, make this harder by standing a tri-fold display board (available at office supply stores) on the table to block the view while one person tries to describe his design in words so the other person can duplicate it.

You can download isometric graph paper from the Incompetech website. Challenge children to build a three-dimensional shape out of blocks and then draw it on the paper. Can you reconstruct their shape from the drawing? Or try to draw an isometric layout of your kitchen, showing all the cabinets, windows, etc.[†]

Most people don't think of pencil and paper as manipulatives, but drafting is a good way to learn geometry, as well as being great fun. Keep drafting tools available. Encourage children to experiment with a protractor, T-square, and compass. Buy quality tools from an office or art supply store. Look for ideas in the free download *Geometry Lessons in the Waldorf School: Freehand Form Drawing and Basic Geometric Construction.*[‡]

Dover Publications offers geometric design coloring books for inspiration. Advanced students can try their hands at Islamic geometric patterns. Download the *Islamic Art and Geometric Design* lessons from the Metropolitan Museum of Art.[§]

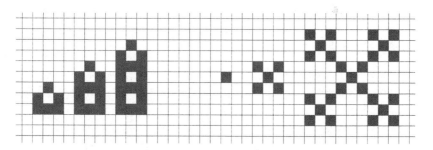

Here are the first three stages of two different growing patterns
on graph paper. How would you describe the changes?
How many squares will we color in the next stage?

[†] *http://incompetech.com/graphpaper/triangle*
[‡] *http://www.waldorflibrary.org/books/3/view_bl/113/form-drawing/120/geometry-lessons-in-the-waldorf-school-ebook*
[§] *http://www.metmuseum.org/~/media/Files/Learn/For%20Educators/Publications%20for%20Educators/Islamic_Art_and_Geometric_Design.pdf (PDF)*

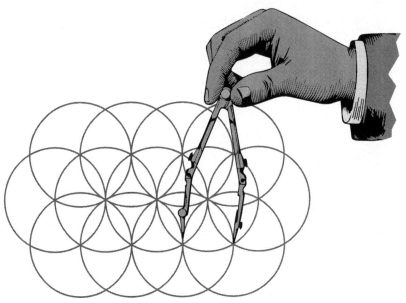

A quality compass will let you draw circles upon circles upon circles without ever changing its radius. But a cheap compass can't even draw a single circle because its radius starts to change as soon as it touches the paper.

Getting a Handle on Abstract Math

Young children can learn algebra if you demonstrate it with manipulatives—even virtual ones, like blocks in a computer program. Most children are eager to play with a new game—and algebra is not just any game, but one normally reserved for teenagers. Try the Dragonbox algebra apps or Henry Borenson's Hands-On Equations for an introduction to algebraic equations.[†]

Spend an afternoon playing with bendable straws for a hands-on exploration of *polygons* (flat shapes such as squares and triangles) or *polyhedra* (three-dimensional shapes such as cubes and pyramids). Pinch the short end of a bendy straw. Slip it into the long end of another straw to connect them. Then add a third straw connecting the other two ends. Presto! A triangle. Four straws make a square. What other shapes can you make? Tape several polygons together to build a polyhedron. Look up the

---

† *http://dragonbox.com*
http://www.borenson.com

Platonic solids online. Can you figure out how to build those?

Many adults are surprised to learn that elementary and middle school children can explore the ideas of calculus. Try some of the activities in Don Cohen's online Map to Calculus. The website is a bit overwhelming at first glance, but anywhere you click, you're bound to find something interesting. I recommend starting with the Infinite Series activity, because many of the other activities build on that.[†]

You can encourage older students to explore the wild worlds of non-Euclidean geometry. The online Taxicab Treasure Hunt game is a good place to start, or read the book *Taxicab Geometry* by Eugene Krause. In taxicab geometry, the shortest distance between two points is not measured "as the crow flies" but as a taxi would drive around the city blocks. This leads to some strange transmutations. For instance, a taxicab circle (all the points a given distance from the center) looks just like a … well, I don't want to give it away.[‡]

For a family that plays with math the mathematician's way, there is always something new to learn. When your children can get their hands on the math and manipulate it, they will be on their way to understanding any tough topic, and the "Aha!" thrill is delicious.

---

† *http://www.mathman.biz/html/map.html*
http://denisegaskins.com/2015/07/02/infinite-cake-don-cohens-infinite-series-for-kids
‡ *http://learner.org/teacherslab/math/geometry/shape/taxicab*
http://faculty.cord.edu/andersod/TaxicabWorksheets.pdf (PDF)

Solving problems is a practical skill
like, let us say, swimming.
We acquire any practical skill
by imitation and practice.

Trying to swim,
you imitate what other people do
with their hands and feet
to keep their heads above water,
and, finally,
you learn to swim by practicing swimming.

Trying to solve problems,
you have to observe and to imitate
what other people do
when solving problems,
and, finally,
you learn to do problems by doing them.

—GEORGE POLYA

A great discovery solves a great problem, but there is a grain of discovery in the solution of any problem.

—GEORGE POLYA

Math That Makes You Think

ARCHIMEDES TRIED TO FIND THE value of π and almost discovered calculus. Pierre de Fermat calculated the result of a gambling game and laid the foundations of probability. Leonhard Euler went for an afternoon walk over the bridges of Königsberg and invented topology. Georg Cantor created a way to count infinity and opened up a whole new world of modern math. Through the centuries, mathematics has grown as mathematicians struggled with and solved challenging problems.

If we want our children to learn math the mathematician's way, we need to offer them plenty of problems to solve. A child may work through several pages of number calculations by rote, following memorized steps, but a good problem demands more attention. A story problem puts flesh on the abstract bones of arithmetic, encouraging the child to ponder what it means for one thing to be bigger than another, or smaller, or faster, or slower, or made up of several parts.

According to American math professor Howard Eves, "There is a distinction between what may be called a problem and what may be considered an exercise. The latter serves to drill a student in some technique or procedure and requires little, if any, original thought. An exercise, then, can always be done with reasonable dispatch and with a minimum of creative thinking."

Eves continued: "In contrast to an exercise, a problem, if it is a good one for its level, should require thought on the part of the student."

Unfortunately, the word problems in many math textbooks are predictable and boring. They are exercises, not true problems. Children just find the key words and apply the proper operation. "How many left?" means to subtract. "How many in all?" means to add or multiply, depending on which chapter we are in.

Where can we find interesting math problems, the kind that challenge our children to think?

One solution is to use the word problems in your text or workbook, but modify them. Read the part that sets up the problem, such as: "Chloe and Tyler like to collect trading cards. Tyler has twenty-four cards more than Chloe." Then ask, "What questions might we ask about this story?" Take dictation, writing your child's ideas on a whiteboard or piece of paper. Then add a little more information: "They have seventy-two cards all together. Now which of your questions can we answer?" Some of the questions may go beyond the data given in the book: "What do we need to know before we can figure that out?" If they want to make up numbers so they can solve it, celebrate their initiative.

My children and I have enjoyed *Math by Kids! A Collection of Word Problems Written by Kids for Kids of All Ages,* edited by Susan Richman. The book has a multitude of problems written by kids from age four to seventeen.

Ed Zaccaro offers a variety of word problems and tips on how to solve them in his *Challenge Math* books and *Becoming a Problem-Solving Genius.* Math contest preparation books are a great resource for word problems that will stretch your students.

For upper-elementary and middle school, check out *Creative Problem Solving in School Mathematics* or *Math Olympiad Contest Problems* by George Lenchner.

For seventh grade, my daughter and I worked through *Competition Math for Middle School* by Jason Batterson. She doesn't like to compete in math contests, but she enjoys problems that make her think—especially when she gets the problem right and I don't. We supplemented the book work with the free, online Alcumus learning system. Alcumus covers topics from prealgebra to algebra 2, geometry, probability, and number theory. Each problem includes a detailed solution, and many are linked to instructional videos as well.[†]

Story Problem Challenge

I love to encourage my math club students to make up their own word problems. They don't have to know how to answer their problems, because we pass the stories around and work on them together. Here are a few of my favorites. For privacy's sake, I have given each student a nickname; the listed age is when they wrote or dictated their stories.

From Chickenfoot, Age 6

I spent $8, and I had $4 left. How much money did I start with? [answer5]

From Princess Kitten, Age 7½

Kelly's family had 5 real dogs. Two of them got lost. Kelly went looking for them. She found 2 stuffed animals that looked like the 2 dogs that got lost. She went back to her home. Then their 3 dogs went looking for the 2 dogs that got lost, and they came back with the 2 dogs and 3 stuffed animals that looked just like the 3 dogs. How many dogs are there altogether? [answer6]

From One of the Three Musketeers, Age 11

Mrs. Sterns has two different recipes of cookies she is going to make. She sees that she does not have any chocolate chips left, so she has to go to the store. But first she has to find out how much to get. One recipe calls for 63 oz. The other calls for 52 oz. When she gets to the store, the only packages they have are 20 oz. of chocolate chips. How many packages should she buy? [answer7]

From the Cowgirl, Age 12

I am an odd number less than 50. I'm square, not prime. And I am divisible by 3. What number am I? [answer8]

† http://www.artofproblemsolving.com/alcumus

From a Musketeer's Sister, Age 13

I take eight counts to do a pirouette turn and two fouettés turns. A pirouette takes ½ of the eight counts. One fouetté takes half that time. How many counts would it take to do the famous combination of one pirouette and 32 fouettés? [answer9]

From Computer Geek, Age 14

You make about $27 profit from selling pineapple soda. If each can costs you 25 cents, and you bought 75 cans and sold 46 cans, how much did you sell each can of soda for? [answer10]

From the Engineer (Dad)

When we went on a fishing vacation to Canada, we found out the grocery stores sold milk in large, 4-liter plastic bags instead of in gallon jugs. Inside each large bag there were three smaller plastic bags. How much milk did each of these smaller bags hold? [answer11]

And My Contribution

The day before the great battle at the Black Gate, a company of 450 orcs camped among the host of Mordor. But an argument broke out over dinner, and ⅓ of them were killed. Then ⅔ of the remainder died when a drunken troll stumbled through their camp during the night. How many of the orcs survived to join the morning's battle? [answer12]

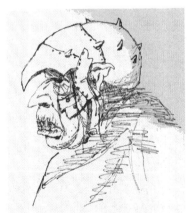

An orc soldier waits for battle. Children will enjoy making up math problems that feature characters from their favorite books and movies.

The Purpose of Word Problems

Word problems feed a student's imagination. In that way, they strengthen mathematical understanding, according to retired professor Andre Toom. Originally from Russia, Toom taught math in several countries around the world, including seven years in American universities.

He writes …

Word problems are very valuable in teaching mathematics—not only to master mathematics, but also for general development.

Especially valuable are word problems solved with minimal scholarship, without algebra, even sometimes without arithmetic, just by plain common sense. The more naive and ingenuous is the solution, the more it provides the child's contact with abstract reality and independence from authority, the more independent and creative thinker the child becomes.

When we teach children to solve problems in school, we do not expect them to meet exactly and literally the same problems in later life. Mathematical education would be next to useless if its only use were literal. We want much more, we want to teach children to solve problems in general. In this respect traditional word problems are especially valuable, because to solve a word problem, you have to understand what is said there.

This function of word problems is very poorly understood in America. The main educative value of word problems is that they serve as mental manipulatives, paving children's road to abstract thinking.

For example, coins, nuts and buttons are clearly distinct and countable, and for this reason are convenient to represent relations between whole numbers. The youngest children need some real, tangible tokens, while older ones can imagine them, which is a further step of intellectual development. That is why coin problems are so appropriate in elementary school.

Pumps and other mechanical appliances are easy to imagine working at a constant rate. Problems involving rate and speed should be (and in Russia are) common already in middle school. Trains, cars and ships are so widely used in textbooks not because all students are expected to go into the transportation business, but for another, much more sound reason: these objects are easy to imagine moving at constant speeds.

There is an important similarity between children's play and mathematics: in both cases, creative imagination is essential.

—Andre Toom

The Language of Word Problems

Most young children solve story problems by the flash-of-insight method: when they read the problem, they know by instinct how to solve it. This is fine for simple problems such as "There are seven children. Two of them are girls. How many boys are there?"

As problems grow more difficult, however, that flash of insight becomes less reliable, so we find our children fidgeting with their paper or staring out the window. They complain, "I don't know what to do. It's too hard."

Our children need a tool that will help them when insight fails.

In the process of solving a word problem, students have to work their way through several steps. They must:

- ◆ Read the problem, and understand what it is asking.

- ◆ Translate the problem situation into a mathematical calculation or algebraic equation.

- ◆ Do the calculation or solve the equation.

- ◆ Interpret the resulting number in the context of the original problem.

Most of the time it is the first two steps that give them trouble. They could do the calculation just fine, if they could decide which calculation to do, but they don't know how to translate the problem from English into "mathish."

Few people realize that a math test is also a test of reading comprehension. In some cases the reading level required far exceeds the level of math. Before they can solve a word problem, children must be able to understand what is written. They must hold that information in their working memory as they think about how to find a solution. They need to comprehend what they read, paraphrase it—concentrating on the relevant facts—and translate that information into a mathematical expression. Frequently they have to read between the lines and understand something that is implied, not explicitly stated.

As English teacher Nick Senger writes, "Paraphrasing is one of the most important skills we can teach junior high and high school students. Often they want to rush into interpreting and reacting to a text even before they know what it means. We teachers sometimes suffer from the delusion that since a student can read the words on the page, he or she understands what's been read. But that's not always true."

If teenagers struggle to interpret their native language, how much more so with math?

Translating English into Math

In addition to the normal challenges of reading, math problems sometimes use familiar words in strange ways. For instance, when a word problem says, "If Joe gave George 23 stickers, how many would he have left?" children tend to get distracted: "Well, what if he didn't? Or what if he gave him 25 of them, or 19?" After all, in normal conversation, the word "if" signals a *maybe or maybe not* situation. But in math problems, the "if" means *for this problem, we are going to assume that the following is true.* There is no *maybe* about it.

Or consider the maddening confusion that may be caused by these two simple statements:

Eight divided in half is four.
Eight divided by one-half is sixteen.

These sentences seem to contradict each other, yet both are true. Can you explain the difference? If your students keep a math journal, you might use this question as a writing prompt.

In the concise language of math problems, small words can make a huge difference. In this case, the prepositions "in" and "by" make the difference between multiplication and division. When you divide a number in half, you are finding *half of* the number—which means multiplication:

$$\tfrac{1}{2} \text{ of } 8 = \tfrac{1}{2} \times 8 = 4$$

But when you divide a number by one-half, you are finding how many

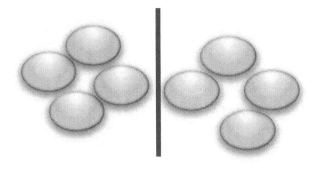

Eight dragon eggs divided in half makes four eggs in each nest.

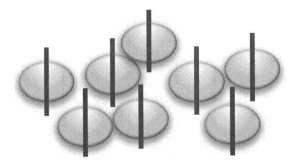

Eight dragon eggs divided by 1/2 is sixteen pieces—or
enough scrambled eggs to feed a whole family of hobbits.

halves it takes to make that number—that is, you are cutting it into half-size pieces and counting how many there are in all. When you do that, because each whole thing splits into two halves, there will be twice as many pieces as the number you started with:

$$8 \div \tfrac{1}{2} = 8 \times 2 = 16$$

If we want to help our children read and make sense of their math problems, we need to show them how to do this sort of translation.

One common classroom approach emphasizes *key* or *signal* words. For instance, we can tell our children that a problem asking, "How many more?" will probably require subtraction. The question asks for the *difference* between two quantities, and difference is the answer when you subtract. But this technique only works for the most simplistic word problems. Indeed, some math problem writers enjoy using key words in ways that will mislead a careless reader.

For example, consider this simple question: "What must we add to 2 to get 7 as the sum?" The key words *add* and *sum* are designed to lead an unwary child into the trap of answering 2 + 7 = 9.

Or what about this one: "There are 21 girls in a class. There are 3 times as many girls as boys. How many boys are in the class?" Would the word *times* trick your child into multiplying?

I do teach a few key words to my students. My favorite is the translation "*of* = *multiply*" when dealing with fraction and percent problems. But I also want my kids to read a math problem and to analyze what is happening, no matter what words are used to describe the situation. For this, they need a more powerful tool than key words.

Bar Model Diagrams

One of my favorite tools for translating word problems into math is a *bar model diagram,* a sort of pictorial algebra in which quantities (both known and unknown) are represented by block-like rectangles. The child imagines moving these blocks around or cutting them into smaller pieces to find a useful relationship between the known and unknown quantities. In this way, the abstract mystery of the word problem becomes a shape puzzle: how can we fit these blocks together? For children who have played with Legos or Cuisenaire rods, this pictorial approach can reveal the underlying structure of a word problem, which helps them relate the problem to similar ones already solved.

All bar diagrams (also called *Singapore math models* or *tape diagrams*) descend from one basic principle, the inverse relationship between addition and subtraction: the whole is the sum of its parts. If you know the value of both parts, you can add them up to get the whole. If you know

whole

| part A | part B |

the whole total and one of the parts, you subtract the part you know to find the other part.

Recall the problem designed to stump a child using key words: "What must we add to 2 to get 7 as the sum?" To figure it out, we could draw a rectangular bar to represent the total amount. Then we would divide it into two parts, representing the number we know and the unknown part. Seven is the sum, the whole thing. What must be the missing part? Now it's easy to see the answer:

When I introduce bar diagrams, I tell my children, "Let's imagine all the items sitting in a row." When a child has trouble figuring out where the numbers go in the diagram, I might ask, "Which is the big amount, the whole thing? What are the parts it is made of?"

As the number relationships in math problems get more complex, the bar may be split into more than two parts. Also, the parts may be related to each other in ways that require a more involved diagram. Multiplication, division, or fraction problems will involve several parts that are the same size, called *units*. But however complicated the story, the solution usually begins by drawing a simple bar to represent one whole thing.

For instance: "There are 21 girls in a class. There are 3 times as many girls as boys. How many boys are in the class?" To show that there are three times as many girls as boys, we can start with a bar for the number of boys. That will be one unit, and then we need three units to show the number of girls. The bar model helps children see that they need to divide, not multiply, to find the number of boys.

I help my children learn to use bar diagrams by not solving the problems. What I mean is, we practice just the tough part, the translation. Once they show me how the bar model would be set up and how they would find the answer, they are done with that problem. The kids suppose they are getting off easy because they don't have to do the multiplication or subtraction or whatever. But I know they've done the real work of reasoning.

If your math program doesn't give your children enough problems to practice on, try the *Challenging Word Problems* series from Singapore Math. Or explore my Word Problems from Literature blog post series or the Thinking Blocks apps and online puzzles.[†]

Let's Try an Example

From time to time, I take one of my children's math tests. It helps me remember what it is like to be a student and helps me understand their point of view. I push myself to work fast, trying to finish in about one-third of the allotted time, to mimic the pressure kids feel. Whenever I do this, I find myself prone to the same stupid mistakes that students make.

In one of these test sessions, I tripped over a multistep word problem, a barrage of information to stumble through. In the middle of it all sat this statement:

> "… and there were ¾ as many dragons as gryphons …"

My eyes saw the words, but my mind heard it this way:

> "… and ¾ of them were dragons …"

What do you think—did I get the answer right? Of course not. Every little word in a math problem is important. Misreading even the smallest word can lead a student astray. My mental glitch encompassed several words, so my final tally of mythological creatures was correspondingly warped.

---

† *http://denisegaskins.com/2010/04/26/word-problems-from-literature*
http://www.thinkingblocks.com

But here is the more important question: can you explain the difference between these two statements?

In my word problem, it turned out there were fifty-six fantasy creatures in all. I got that part of the answer, but then I needed to find the number of gryphons. This is how I did it:

"... and ¾ of them were dragons ..."

Imagine all fifty-six creatures in a zoo, split evenly into four pens. Three of the pens hold various breeds of dragon, and the fourth pen has the gryphons.

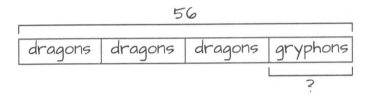

4 pens = 56 creatures

1 pen = 56 ÷ 4 = 14 gryphons

But that was not at all what the problem said. In the true scenario, the number of dragons ought to be fewer than the number of gryphons—a mere three-fourths as many—so my solution has too many dragons. My answer fails the common-sense test.

If I had been paying better attention to what I read, this is how I should have solved the problem:

"... and there were ¾ as many dragons as gryphons ..."

This zoo is wiser than the first one, because it splits the troublesome creatures into smaller groups, so there's less chance of a fight that might endanger visitors. The gryphons are split into four pens, so each pen holds one-fourth of the gryphons. The dragons have three pens all to themselves, which makes three-fourths as many as the gryphons. Thus we have a total of seven fenced-in areas.

$$7 \text{ pens} = 56 \text{ creatures}$$
$$1 \text{ pen} = 56 \div 7 = 8 \text{ creatures per pen}$$
$$4 \text{ pens} = 4 \times 8 = 32 \text{ gryphons}$$

To make the reading issue more difficult, consider this: all the statements in the following list are equivalent. Compare each statement to the second diagram, the correct one. Can you see each relationship?

- There are 25% fewer dragons than gryphons.
- For every four gryphons, there are three dragons.
- The ratio of dragons to gryphons is 3:4.
- Four out of every seven creatures is a gryphon.
- There are one-third more gryphons than dragons.
- There are one-fourth fewer dragons than gryphons.
- If you tag a creature at random from the group, the probability of choosing a dragon is three-sevenths.

Can you think of any other ways to say it? This would be another good math journal writing prompt.

A Guide to Solving Word Problems

Math professor Herb Gross says: "As important as mathematics is, it is a distant second to the need for good reading comprehension. We teachers so often hear students summarize a course by saying, 'I could do everything except the word problems.' Sadly, in the textbook of life, there are only word problems."

The more we can work with our children on reading, paraphrasing, and translating word problems into mathematical expressions, the better prepared they will be to face the challenges they will meet in future math classes and in the textbook of life.

Here is a four-step approach that will help children at any grade level think their way through a tough problem. The following questions represent a common-sense approach to solving any problem, which means students can learn to ask them for themselves.

Ask Yourself These Four Questions

- ♦ What do I know?
- ♦ What do I want?
- ♦ What can I do?
- ♦ Does it make sense?

(1) What Do I Know?

Read the problem carefully. Reread it until you can describe the situation in your own words. List the facts or information given in the problem. Underline or circle any important words, such as *factor, multiple, area,* or *perimeter.* What do you remember about those topics? Watch out for mixed units.

Express the facts in math symbols, if you can.

(2) What Do I Want?

Describe the goal, what the problem is asking you to find. Underline or circle any important words, such as *sum, product, next,* or *not.* Small words such as "not" are easy to miss.

Express the goal in math symbols, if you can.

(3) What Can I Do?

Combine the given facts. Even if you can't solve the problem, can you think of a way to get closer to your goal? Take one little step at a time.

Try a tool from your problem-solving toolbox:

- ♦ Draw a diagram or picture.
- ♦ Act the problem out, step by step.

- Make a systematic list, chart, or table.

- Look for a pattern.

- Simplify the problem. (Try it with smaller numbers.)

- Restate the problem in another way, or look for a related problem.

- Think about "Before" and "After" situations.

- Work backward.

- Guess and check. (Try something to see if it works.)

(4) Does It Make Sense?

Don't neglect this last step! When you think you have found the answer, always look back at the original problem one more time. Do you have the correct units (inches, cm², kg, etc.)? Does your answer make sense in the problem situation?

Can you think of a way to confirm that your answer is right?

Your Child's Most Important Math Manipulative

Any math student's most valuable hands-on problem-solving tool will be a pad of scratch paper. Pencil and paper become an extension of our brain, a way to organize our thoughts as we tackle a new problem.

Like fingers, those built-in manipulatives, paper is familiar and always available. Children have already drawn pictures, written letters, or folded and decorated paper airplanes. Now you can show your kids how to draw dots for grouping in a multiplication problem, keep a tally of heads and tails coin flips, or diagram the travels of a rocket starting at $v_0 = 0$ mph and accelerating at rate a for time t.

Wise students will tackle any tough problem by drawing a simple, stick-figure sketch and writing down everything they know about the situation. A sketch is like thinking aloud on paper, doodling, working their way toward understanding the problem. This sort of brainstorming often suggests a new approach or points the way to a solution.

When students learn to sketch, some problems almost solve themselves.

For instance, if we need to find the ground speed of an airplane, we might draw the angle between air speed and crosswinds. Here is the plane flying, and this is the wind. Aha! The wind blows the plane sideways, and here is the angle…

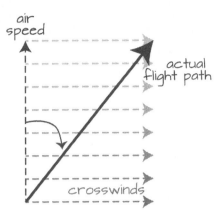

Yet even college students try to skip this step, believing that they are taking a short cut. They balk at sketching ("I can't draw"), and they don't see how writing things down will help them think. So they wait for the answer to pop into their heads fully formed. Then when the solution does not appear like magic, they complain that math is too hard.

Encourage your children to approach problem solving as they would a jigsaw puzzle:

- ◆ The sketch helps them visualize what is happening, like the picture on the box helps the puzzler see his goal.

- ◆ When children start moving pieces of the puzzle around, they look for the easy parts first, perhaps the edge pieces or the eyes. In the same way, wise math problem solvers tackle the easiest-to-understand parts of their puzzle first.

- ◆ As children get into a jigsaw puzzle, they may try several pieces that don't work, so they set them aside and try others. Likewise, math students need not be discouraged by mistakes or false starts because they know mistakes are part of the game.

Let's see how this works on a few traditional brain teasers.

The Hungry Bookworm

Living in the country, I am used to having nature's critters saunter up to my door and make themselves at home. But chewing on my books? Now that means war. Pretend a famished bookworm did manage to make it to my shelves, however, and chowed down on our *Golden Book Encyclopedia* set. The nasty thing started at page one of the A's and nibbled its way straight through to the end of the Z's. If each of the sixteen volumes is one-half inch thick, how far did the bookworm travel? (To make the figuring easier, ignore the covers of the books.)

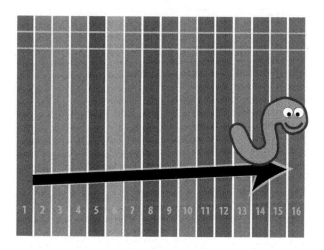

I can calculate the total thickness of the set: 16 × ½ = 8 inches. If I don't stop to draw a picture or walk over to the shelf to look at the books, I will assume that the obvious answer is eight inches. I would be wrong.

The thing is, because we read English from left to right, the books are bound on their left-hand side. That means, when we stack them in numerical order on a shelf, the front of volume one touches the back of volume two. The front of volume two touches the back of volume three. And so on down the line, until the front of the next-to-last book touches the back of the last one in the row.

Starting at page one of the A's and tunneling toward the Z's, the bookworm will miss almost the entire first book. It eats one page, thin enough not to affect the total length of the journey. In the same way, the back of volume sixteen is touching the front of volume fifteen, so the worm would reach the last page of the Z's without eating enough of that book to count.

The total path is 14 × ½ = 7 inches long.

The Frog in the Well

A hapless frog wanders into a cottage garden in search of bugs, and lands unhoppily at the bottom of a fifty-foot wishing well. Scrambling up the slippery slime, he manages to climb four feet up the side of the well every day, but he slides back down two feet every night. At least there are flies buzzing about to keep up his strength. How many days will it be before the frog regains his freedom?

At first glance, the solution seems obvious. With a net gain of two feet per day, the frog has twenty-five days of climbing to go. But if the obvious answer were the correct one, this wouldn't be a brainteaser, right?

When I draw a sketch of the well and start to count up the frog's progress, I notice that his daily climb takes him two feet past each day's net gain. That is, on the first day, the frog scrambles 2 + 2 = 4 feet then slides back down. On the second day, he climbs to 4 + 2 = 6 feet before he slips back. On the third day, he gets as high as 6 + 2 = 8 feet, then takes a gooey skid downward.

Start by imagining the problem with smaller numbers. Here is a twelve-foot well. Each color represents one day's climb and slide back down.

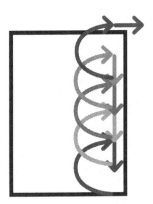

On the twenty-fourth day, the frog reaches (24 × 2) + 2 = 48 + 2 = 50 feet, and he hops out into the garden. So it takes the frog twenty-four days to escape, not the twenty-five days I first expected.

Now You Try It: The New Family

While checking out the book table after a math circle meeting, you glance up to see your children laughing with some kids you don't recognize. On the drive home, you quiz your children about the new family, but they don't have much information to share. They were too busy exchanging silly jokes to even ask the strangers' names.

"Oh, I remember one thing," your son says. "The boy said he had twice as many sisters as brothers."

"No way!" your daughter protests. "The girl said she had the same number of brothers and sisters."

How is it possible for both statements to be true? [answer13]

One More Source of Challenging Math Problems

Mathematics began with practical problems like the following:

♦ How can we measure this farmer's field, so we can collect the proper amount of taxes for Pharaoh?

♦ How can we predict the winter solstice, so we can schedule our religious festival?

♦ How can we divide six loaves of bread among eleven construction workers?

As the centuries passed, however, mathematicians became interested in more abstract puzzles. They started to wonder about such questions as:

♦ How can we know that the angles in a triangle add up to the same as a straight line?

♦ Is there a largest prime number?

♦ How big is infinity?

"It is impossible to overstate the importance of problems in mathematics," according to Howard Eves, who wrote an influential textbook on math history. "It is by means of problems that mathematics develops and actually lifts itself by its own bootstraps. Every new discovery in mathematics results from an attempt to solve some problem."

If we're looking for math problems to challenge our children, math history is the mother lode. A rich supply of interesting puzzles is as near as the public library.

I know you may bring a horse to the water,
but you cannot make him drink.
What I complain of is that
we do not bring our horse to the water.
We give him miserable little textbooks,
mere compendiums of facts,
which he is to learn off and say and produce at an examination.

And all the time we have books,
books teeming with ideas
fresh from the minds of thinkers
upon every subject to which we can wish to introduce children.

We must open books to children,
the best books.
For the mind is capable of dealing
with only one kind of food;
it lives, grows and is nourished upon ideas only;
mere information is to it as a meal of sawdust to the body.

Our business is to give our children mind-stuff,
and both quality and quantity are essential.
Naturally, each of us possesses this mind-stuff
only in limited measure,
but we know where to procure it;
for the best thought the world possesses is stored in books.

—CHARLOTTE MASON

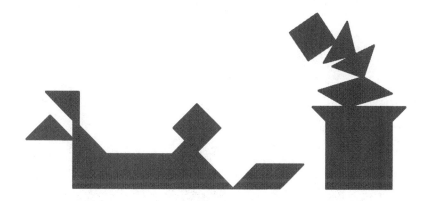

Math with Living Books

In most sciences, one generation tears down what another has built, and what one has established another undoes. In mathematics alone, each generation adds a new story to the old structure.

—HERMANN HANKEL

Math You Can Read

ONE OF BARON JOHN NAPIER'S servants was stealing from him, so the baron devised a plan. He set his black rooster on a table in the middle of a small, dimly-lit room. Then he sent the servants one by one into the room, with instructions to stroke the rooster's back. The rooster was enchanted, he said, and it would tell him who had taken his silver.

Napier had coated the rooster's feathers with soot. Knowing the servants were superstitious, he was sure the guilty person would not dare to touch the supposedly-magical rooster. Therefore, whoever came out of the room with clean hands must be the thief.

What does this have to do with mathematics? Math was Napier's favorite hobby. In 1614, he published a book about logarithms, which he had invented to help people calculate with large numbers. Napier also created a method of using a chessboard to solve arithmetic problems (instructions in the next chapter, page 131).

The story of mathematics is the story of interesting people. They faced the normal challenges of daily life as well as the creative challenges of mathematical imagination. For some, calculation and problem solving seemed as natural as breathing. Others worked for years in fits and starts before reaching a solution. Some had long and happy lives. Others died tragically young.

English physicist and mathematician Isaac Newton caused a UFO scare by flying a kite that carried a lantern. As a boy in the mid-seventeenth century, Newton was a poor student who only became a scholar in order to show up the class bully.

Though he claimed to have invented calculus in 1666, Newton didn't announce his work until decades later. In the meantime, German mathematician Gottfried Wilhelm Leibniz had published his own version. By the end of the century, English and German scholars were embroiled in the original Math War over which man (and thus which country) deserved the credit.

Maria Agnesi solved math problems while sleepwalking. When she got stumped, she left the problem on her desk and went to bed. The next morning, she found the correct solution neatly written on her paper.

After teaching calculus to her younger brothers, in 1748 Agnesi published what became Europe's most popular calculus textbook for the next fifty years. Still, there was something she loved more than math: she longed to become a nun, but her father would not allow it. After her father died, she devoted the rest of her life to helping the poor and homeless.

As a child in the mid-nineteenth century, Sofia (Sonya) Kovalevskaya became intrigued with math from reading her bedroom wall, papered with her father's old calculus lecture notes. To escape Russia, where women were not allowed to study mathematics, she arranged a marriage of convenience. When her husband died, she struggled on as a single mother. Kovalevskaya won a prestigious prize for original mathematical research, and her paper was so brilliant that the judges increased the prize to almost double what they usually awarded.

Born in colonial India, Srinivasa Ramanujan taught himself math. In the late nineteenth century, mathematics was advancing at a rapid pace in

Europe, but Ramanujan flunked out of college (being unwilling to put effort into any of his studies except math). In his poverty and isolation he was unaware of modern discoveries. When he came to Europe and spent a few years working with Cambridge professors G. H. Hardy and John Littlewood, Ramanujan had trouble understanding the idea of a systematic mathematical proof. He loved playing around with numbers, looking for patterns, and he was used to making wildly intuitive leaps from one idea to another which others found difficult to follow. After he died at the age of thirty-two, his notebooks provided many years' worth of research fodder for Hardy and other mathematicians.

ooooooooo

What a shame it is that our children see nothing but the dry remains of these people's passion. Worksheet exercises are the bare, abstract skeletons of what were once living puzzles. As Victorian-era math professor James Glaisher once said, "I am sure that no subject loses more than mathematics by any attempt to dissociate it from its history."

Math and history—what can they have in common? After all, history is all about kings and wars, while math is numbers and rules. Isn't it?

"Biographical history, as taught in our public schools, is still largely a story of boneheads: ridiculous kings and queens, paranoid political leaders, compulsive voyagers, ignorant generals, the flotsam and jetsam of historical currents," according to popular math writer Martin Gardner. "The men who radically altered history, the great scientists and mathematicians, are seldom mentioned, if at all."

It does not have to be that way for our children. By reading math history, we can help our students build a mental picture of the ebb and flow of ideas through the centuries. They will see how men and women grappled with concepts, made mistakes, argued with each other, and bit by bit developed the knowledge that today we take for granted.

Bringing Math to Life

Most parents, whatever our curriculum or schooling approach, understand the importance of reading real books—the kind that Victorian educator Charlotte Mason called *living* books. We read aloud to our children, introducing them to biographies, historical fiction, or the classics of literature. We scour library shelves for the most creative presentations of scientific topics to spark their interest. We encourage our teenagers to go back to the original documents whenever possible.

But many children rarely see math outside a textbook.

One reason for this imbalance is that most adults never learned math history ourselves. We may not even be aware that math has a history. Our school experience made mathematics seem like something handed down from on high, to be accepted and memorized, never to be challenged.

Fortunately, when we decide to embark on a tour of math history, we won't have to go it alone. Several entertaining and knowledgeable guides are available. Some of them may be sitting on the shelf at your local library right now, waiting to lead you along the way.

You can begin exploring the excitement of mathematics with young children through picture books. *What's Your Angle, Pythagoras?* by Julie Ellis offers a fanciful look at the childhood of that famous mathematician. Or read about the man who brought mathematics back to Europe after the Dark Ages in *Blockhead: The Life of Fibonacci* by Joseph D'Agnese.

For beginning readers: *A Fly on the Ceiling* by Julie Glass will make children laugh while they learn about René Descartes, the father of analytic geometry. *Ben Franklin and the Magic Squares* by Frank Murphy tells a lively story about one of old Ben's favorite pastimes.

Older children can enjoy picture books, too. *The Librarian Who Measured the Earth* by Kathryn Lasky tells how the Greek scholar Eratosthenes calculated the circumference of the earth using sunlight and shadows. Skip forward to the colonial era with *Dear Benjamin Banneker* by Andrea Davis Pinkney, the life story of a self-taught African-American astronomer and mathematician.

The Wonderful World of Mathematics by Lancelot Hogben will give your children a great overview of math in many cultures from Ancient Egypt to the Industrial Revolution. It is out of print, but I've spotted used copies at several online bookstores.

Mathematicians Are People, Too by Luetta and Wilbert Reimer features short, fictionalized vignettes for reading aloud to elementary students. The Reimers also wrote a three-volume reference series called *Historical*

Connections in Mathematics: Resources for Using History of Mathematics in the Classroom, which offers the basic facts and anecdotes about each mathematician without fictional elaboration—as a bonus, it includes related worksheets.

Treat your older children (and yourself) to a few of our family favorites. *Archimedes and the Door of Science* by Jeanne Bendick describes the life and discoveries of one of the greatest mathematicians who ever lived. *Carry On, Mr. Bowditch* by Jean Lee Latham tells the inspiring story of an eighteenth-century American hero whose mathematical studies saved the lives of countless sailors. *Count Like an Egyptian: A Hands-on Introduction to Ancient Mathematics* by David Reimer offers a new (yet very old) way of looking at numbers.

High school students will enjoy *Famous Problems and Their Mathematicians* by Art Johnson. Another combination of anecdotes and activities, the book touches on many of the ideas that have intrigued mathematicians for centuries.

William Dunham writes for the general adult audience, but many teenagers will find his books compelling. *The Mathematical Universe* offers an A-to-Z smorgasbord of math topics and people. *Journey through Genius* follows the development of several discoveries by the great masters of mathematics.

If you want more complete biographies, start with *Of Men and Numbers: The Story of the Great Mathematicians* by Jane Muir. For high school students, try *Men of Mathematics* by Eric Temple Bell. Bell tells the stories of more than two dozen mathematicians who laid the foundations for modern mathematics, with Sofia Kovalevskaya included as a sort of "honorary" man. But be warned: the author gets so caught up in his stories that he sometimes lapses into pure, over-romanticized fiction.

The newer, five-volume *Pioneers in Mathematics* series by Michael J. Bradley features biographies of significant mathematicians from Ancient Greece to the present day. Keith Devlin provides insight into historical and modern math in *The Language of Mathematics: Making the Invisible Visible*. These books cover a wide range of topics and give readers an idea of what modern mathematicians do for a living.

A four-volume series called *The World of Mathematics* is a fantastic resource for older readers. Not a mathematician himself, editor James Newman collected articles by eminent mathematicians and other thinkers that were both interesting and accessible to the adult layman. "From A'hmose the Scribe to Albert Einstein, presented with commentaries and notes."

Playful Math You Can Read

Moving beyond history, your local library can provide a variety of books that bring math concepts alive with color, flair, and projects to try. If you have access to interlibrary loan, you can obtain almost any book in print within weeks. Most of the newer books are also available in digital formats.

For young children, look for shape, counting, and concept books, and as they grow, add anything by Greg Tang or Mitsumasa Anno. Read Christopher Danielson's *Talking Math with Your Kids* and learn how to start discussions about the numbers, shapes, and patterns in your child's daily life. Children who love knights and princesses will enjoy the *Sir Cumference* series. Explore the many hands-on activity ideas in *Moebius Noodles: Adventurous Math for the Playground Crowd* by Maria Droujkova and Yelena McManaman. Try some of the activities in Lore Rasmussen's *First Grade Diary*. Don't miss *Games for Math* by Peggy Kaye.

When your children reach school age, check the J510–519 range in the Dewey decimal system for creative introductions to a variety of mathematical ideas. The Time-Life *I Love Math* series is wonderful, as is the Crowell *Young Math Book* series, both of which are out of print but well worth buying used. Invite your child's friends over to share cookies and math, with a game from *Family Math* by Stenmark, et al., or one of the activities from *Math for Smarty Pants* by Marilyn Burns.

Read aloud mathematical fiction, such as *The Cat in Numberland* by Ivar Ekeland, *The Man Who Counted* by Malba Tahan, or *The Number Devil* by Hans Magnus Enzensberger. Older children will enjoy the *Murderous Maths* series by Kjartan Poskitt, *The 'I Hate Mathematics!' Book* by Marilyn Burns, or *Math Games & Activities from Around the World* by Claudia Zaslavsky. Investigate the problem-solving books listed in Chapter 5, and explore the J793.74 shelf for riddles and logic puzzles.

In middle school, my daughter's favorite math books were *Math Doesn't Suck: How to Survive Middle School Math without Losing Your Mind or Breaking a Nail* and its sequels by Danica McKellar. Students at that age may also want to venture into the adult shelves, starting with the 793.74 puzzle books. Anything by Brian Bolt is diverting: short, brain-bending teasers and games illustrated with cartoons.

Teenagers will enjoy the logic puzzles of Raymond Smullyan. *The Joy of x: A Guided Tour of Math, from One to Infinity* by Steven Strogatz shows how math connects to every aspect of life. Martin Gardner's many collections of games, puzzles, and mathematical tidbits from his days as a *Scientific American* columnist may inspire a true love of mathematics.

High school students may also be ready to explore the adult 510–519 shelves. But do watch out for books written in an alien tongue; some mathematicians suffer from technical-journal-itis whenever they pick up a pen. When your children find a book like this, shrug it off and try again. Here's my general rule for learning about math from people smarter than me: read the introduction and keep going as long as I find it interesting. When the author starts talking about stuff that's over my head, I feel free to stop. I may not finish all the books I pick up, but I'm always learning new things.

Does all of this whet your appetite for reading about math? For more tasty temptations, check the appendix "Living Math Books for All Ages" (page 211) and Julie Brennan's extensive book lists at LivingMath.net. If you would like a whole math program built around living books and related activities, Julie published a four-year cycle of *Living Math History Lesson Plans.*†

---

† *http://livingmath.net/ReaderLists/tabid/268/Default.aspx*
http://livingmath.net/LessonPlans/LessonPlanInformation/tabid/1002/Default.aspx

The Trouble with History

Be aware, however, that any outline of mathematical history is by necessity sketchy and incomplete, with many of the dates being mere approximation. Our view of long ago is fogged with a mixture of myth, legend, and uncertainty.

Imagine waiting at the end of a long line in the children's party game of Telephone. The first player reads a short paragraph to the next person, who tries to repeat it to the player after him, continuing on down the line until the garbled version reaches your ears. Can you figure out the original message?

That is about how historians have reconstructed some ancient Greek texts. Suppose one mathematician gave a lecture about his discovery at Plato's Academy. Someone else heard about it and told it to his friend, who mentioned it in a letter to another mathematician, who referred to it in the book he was writing. Then that book was passed along and copied a few dozen times (parchment deteriorates), and perhaps a copy of a copy of a copy has survived. Or maybe another ancient writer quoted the book in his own masterpiece, and a multi-generation copy of that is what historians have today.

When you think about it, it's amazing we know anything about the original lecturer. It makes me wonder what else those old gentlemen discovered that has been forever lost.

Then again, picture yourself walking into a room where two children are fighting. How do you sort out the "He started it!" and "She pinched me first!" arguments? Now imagine having to do that for an event that happened three centuries ago. That will help you imagine the problem historians face in deciphering the often-conflicting diaries, letters, and other documents left by the mathematicians of the seventeenth and eighteenth centuries. "I thought of it first ... He copied from me ... Your proof wasn't valid, anyway ... It's not fair!"

Or consider Sofia Kovalevskaya, who also went by the name of Sonya. In some sources, her name is spelled Sophie or Sophia or Kowalewski. That is a minor point to us, since the names are close enough to be recognized, although I imagine it would have mattered more to her. But other mathematicians had nicknames that were different enough to make it confusing whether a writer is talking about one man or two.

Or two different men may have the same name. Hippocrates of Chios, the mathematician, is not the same as Hippocrates of Cos, the doctor.

When you meet one of these mix-ups in your reading, help your children understand the challenges of historical interpretation. They will gain a more mature understanding of all history, not just the history of math.

Page from *The Compendious Book on Calculation by Completion and Balancing* by Muhammad ibn Mūsā al-Khwārizmī (c. AD 820), the world's first algebra textbook.

*Compared to what glorious Greece did in mathematics,
the nineteenth century is a bonfire beside a penny candle.*

—E. T. BELL

4,000 Years of Stumpers

FROM THE SCRIBES OF ANCIENT Egypt to the modern college professor, mathematicians have always enjoyed puzzles. What better way to get a quick overview of mathematics than with a few problems from across the ages?

Alfred North Whitehead, one of the pioneers of mathematical philosophy, wrote: "I will not go so far as to say that to construct a history of thought without profound study of the mathematical ideas of successive epochs is like omitting Hamlet from the play which is named after him. That would be claiming too much. But it is certainly analogous to cutting out the part of Ophelia. This simile is singularly exact. For Ophelia is quite essential to the play, she is very charming … and a little mad."

As you and your children work your way through world history, take time now and then to investigate what sort of "charming and a little mad" mathematics was happening in each era. Help your students build a mental picture of how ideas grew over time.

In the following outline, I've included at least one sample activity related to each time period. One of the primary joys of sharing math as a family is that we adults can grow in our own understanding by learning and playing along. Find one or two puzzles that look interesting enough to try with your children. Many of the challenges in this chapter are easy

119

enough for elementary students. Others are more suited for high school.

As with the other puzzles in this book, the answers are included in the appendix. If you need to look up an answer, don't view that as a failure in your mathematical skills. See it instead as an opportunity to learn something new (or to refresh a weak spot in your memory) by taking that answer and working backward. As we analyze how mathematicians solved these puzzles, we grow in our understanding of math and of history.

Egypt and Babylonia

3000 BC–330 BC

The Babylonians and Egyptians had great empires to rule, which meant records had to be kept and property to be taxed. Astronomical charts and calendars were important, so that crops could be planted and festivals celebrated at the proper time. Much of their mathematics derived from the question, "How can I count it or measure it?"

Both cultures were interested in arithmetic and practical geometry, reasoning inductively from specific examples to find more general principles. They also learned to solve certain types of equations, and the Babylonians recorded long charts such as the times tables or lists of square numbers. The Egyptians used a decimal (base ten) system without place value, similar to Roman numerals, while in Babylonia they used a sexagesimal (base sixty) number system that included place value but lacked a symbol for zero.

We know only one mathematician from this period by name: A'hmose, an Egyptian scribe.

A'hmose's Secret Number Puzzle

The scribe A'hmose wrote what we now call the Rhind papyrus in about 1650 BC. It may have been a homework assignment for scribe school, or perhaps he was the teacher and wrote it for his students. He included a huge table of fractions and plenty of story problems, geometry, simple algebra, and accounting. Most of the calculations were written as specific examples, such as how to divide loaves of bread and barrels of beer to pay a given number of workers. Students who understood an example could then follow the same method to work other, similar problems.

Here is a "magic" trick from the Rhind papyrus. But be forewarned: the Egyptian scribes loved the challenge of working with fractions. To use the magic trick, you and your friend will need to find fractional parts of various numbers. These calculations will be easier if you tell your friend to make sure his secret number is a multiple of nine.

- Tell your friend to think of a secret number. For example, your friend might start by choosing 36.

- Then have him add two-thirds more of his number but not tell you the answer. One-third of thirty-six is twelve, so two-thirds is twenty-four. Your friend would add 36 + 24 = 60.

- Finally, tell him to take away one-third of this total and to say this answer. Since one-third of sixty is twenty, and 60 – 20 = 40, your friend would say, "Forty."

- Now you must subtract one-tenth of this number to find his secret number. In our example, 40 – 4 = 36.

Bonus puzzle for students who know algebra: can you show why this trick will work for any number? Can you make up a "mathemagic" trick of your own? [answer14]

Ancient China

2000 BC–1600 CE

Because China was isolated from the rest of the world through much of history, Chinese mathematics has a character all its own. Like the Egyptians and Babylonians, mathematicians in ancient China worked on problems concerning astronomy and the calendar, measurement and record-keeping, and the surveying of land for taxes. From these problems, they built their knowledge of mathematics. They used a decimal number system and did calculations on a counting board.

The Chinese knew about and calculated the series of numbers we now know as Pascal's Triangle many centuries before Pascal was born. They also knew and used the Pythagorean Theorem, solved several types of equations, and developed trigonometry. The Chinese Remainder Theorem is probably beyond your children's skill level, but they might enjoy creating simple remainder problems. For instance:

♦ How many soldiers are there in the emperor's royal guard? If they parade in rows of three, two soldiers will be left out. In rows of five, three men will be left. And in rows of six, five will remain. [answer15]

Mathematicians include Liu Hui, Sun Zi, Zhang Qiujian, Zu Chongzhi and his son Zu Geng, Wang Xiaotong, Qin Jiushao, Li Zhi, Yang Hui, and Zhu Shijie.

The Emperor and the Tortoise

In the old days, Chinese people called the Yellow River (Huang He) valley the "Middle Kingdom"—the center of the world. According to legend, the Emperor Yu (c. 2200 BC) was traveling along the Yellow River one day when he spotted the divine tortoise Lo Shu on the bank. Lo Shu's back was decorated with a magic square, which Emperor Yu adopted as a good luck charm.

Here is a picture of the tortoise Lo Shu. Can you figure out what the shapes mean? Why are some of the dots white while others are black? [answer16]

Ancient Greece

600 BC–550 CE

Sometime around 600 BC, a revolution in thinking occurred. A young Greek merchant named Thales began to ask not only how things worked, but also why. His emphasis on reasoning set Greek philosophy on the course of logic and deductive proof. Thus mathematics as we now understand it was born.

The key question that interested Greek mathematicians was, "How can I prove it?" Geometry was an important foundation of Greek mathematics. Diagrams were often scratched in sand with a compass and straightedge (like a ruler but without markings). Later work was done on papyrus, a convenient but fragile medium. The Pythagoreans investigated *number theory*—the relationships between numbers—but even there they used geometry. A number was considered as a length (of string, for example, perhaps on a musical instrument), not something abstract in itself. Later mathematicians at Alexandria in Egypt studied conic section curves, such as the parabola and ellipse. Archimedes analyzed infinite series and developed many of the ideas that would lead to calculus.

Mathematicians include Thales, Pythagoras, Hippocrates of Chios, Plato, Eudoxus, Aristotle, Euclid, Pappus, Diophantus, Archimedes, Apollonius, Ptolemy, Hipparchus, Menelaus, Heron, and Hypatia (the first known woman mathematician).

Thales, the First Mathematician

In his hometown of Miletus (on the coast of what is now Turkey), Thales was well known as a businessman, engineer, philosopher, statesman, astronomer, mathematician, and the quintessential absent-minded professor. According to rumor, one night he went for a walk, and as he gazed up at the stars, he fell into an open well.

Thales left us no writings of his own, but according to Aristotle and other Greek historians, he proved the following geometric theorems. (*Congruent* is for geometric objects what *equal* is for numbers—it means they have the same size and shape.)

- Whenever two straight lines cross, the angles opposite each other must be congruent.

- If two sides of a triangle have equal lengths, then the angles opposite those sides must be congruent.

- If triangles have two angles and one side congruent, then the triangles are congruent.

- Any *diameter* (straight line through the center) cuts a circle in half.

- Any angle drawn with its corner on a circle and its rays going through the endpoints of the circle's diameter must be a right angle.

Thales used his knowledge to astonish the people around him. While in Egypt, he determined the height of the Great Pyramid at Giza by measuring its shadow. At that time, the pyramids were already more than 2,000 years old.

Back home in Miletus, he was able to stand on shore—perhaps on a cliff or tall building—and measure the distance to a ship at sea. To find the distance to the ship, Thales may have used a hinged rod like the one shown here. How might this help him describe a triangle that, along with one of the theorems above, would help him find the distance to the ship? [answer17]

Thales of Miletus, father of Ancient Greek mathematics and philosophy.

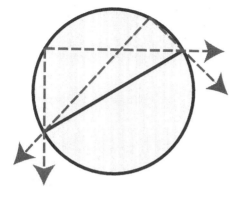

Thales' theorem:
If we have a circle and
one of its diameters,
we can draw an infinite
number of right angles.

Ancient India

200 BC–1450

We owe a great debt to the early mathematicians of the Indus River area, who invented an efficient decimal place-value system that (eventually) included zero. This was later adopted by the Arabs and developed into our modern numbers.

As in the other ancient civilizations, mathematicians in India developed geometry and solved equations in order to build their temples and to study astronomy. Hindu mathematicians were intrigued by large numbers and by the idea of infinity. They also experimented with negative numbers.

Mathematicians include Varāhamihira, two different men named Aryabhata, Brahmagupta, Mahāvīra, Mādhava, and two different men named Bhāskara.

Bhāskara's Beautiful Book

The second (and more famous) Bhāskara is also known as Bhāskarāchārya, or "Bhāskara the Teacher." He was an Indian mathematician and astronomer who lived in the early part of the twelfth century. Bhāskara must have loved math, for he named his book about arithmetic *Lilāvati*, which means "The Beautiful." He also wrote about algebra, geometry, trigonometry, and calculus, which would not be discovered by Europeans for several centuries.

Here are a few of Bhāskara's arithmetic problems for middle school students, taken from the 1816 translation by John Taylor:[†]

- ♦ One-third of a collection of beautiful water lilies is offered to Mahadev, one-fifth to Huri, one-sixth to the Sun, one-fourth to Devi, and six which remain are presented to the spiritual teacher. Required: the whole number of water lilies? [answer18]

- ♦ A traveler pays away one-half at Pryag; from the remainder he pays two-ninths at Benares; from the remainder he pays one-fourth for customs and other fees; from the remainder six-tenths are paid at Gaya; and there remain sixty-three which he brings home. What was the original sum? [answer19]

- ♦ One-fifth of a hive of bees flew to the Kadamba flower; one-third flew to the Silandhara; three times the difference of these two numbers flew to an arbour; and one bee continued flying about, attracted on each side by the fragrant Ketaki and the Malati. What was the number of bees? [answer20]

Here is a geometric challenge for high school students. Examine the following diagram, called Bhāskara's Dissection, where a large square is cut apart into four congruent right triangles and a small square, which are then rearranged to make a second shape. Can you tell which famous theorem his drawing proves? [answer21]

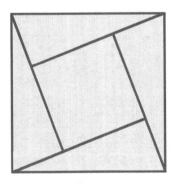 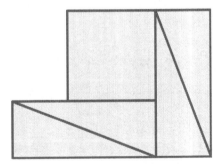

† http://books.google.com/books?id=OKMIAAAAQAAJ

Arab Empires

780–1400

In the late eighth century, Baghdad became a center of learning, where Arab mathematicians gathered and synthesized math from all around the known world. Due to the Euro-centrism of past historians, the Arabs are best known for keeping the knowledge of the Greeks alive through the European Dark Ages and for bringing the ideas of Hindu mathematicians to the West. The mathematicians of the Arab empires were quite skilled in their own right, however, and they discovered and developed many mathematical ideas centuries before the Europeans thought of such things.

The most important Arab innovation was the idea of algebra, of calculating with unknown numbers. Earlier mathematicians could solve a few equations by using rules of thumb discovered over the centuries. Algebra opened a whole new world of abstract mathematical understanding. By translating geometric problems into algebra, Arab mathematicians could apply the rules of arithmetic to them, leading to advances in number theory, trigonometry, and many other areas of study.

Mathematicians include Muhammad ibn Mūsā al-Khwārizmī, Al-Māhānī, Thābit ibn Qurra and his grandson Ibrahim, Abū al-Wafā' Būzjānī, Al-Karajī, Omar Khayyám, and Samau'al al-Maghribi.

Al-Khwārizmī's Algebra

Al-Khwārizmī wrote what he called "a short work on calculating by *al-jabr* and *al-muqabala,* confining it to what is easiest and most useful in arithmetic." This is probably one of the books Fibonacci brought back from his travels (see the next section). We get our modern term *algebra* from this *al-jabr,* which means "restoring" and refers to a method of simplifying equations.

The first part of al-Khwārizmī's book described how to solve equations. Then he explored practical story problems about inheritance, lawsuits, trade, digging canals, and more. However, al-Khwārizmī knew nothing about the type of algebraic notation we use today, where letters can stand in for unknown numbers. He wrote each of his equations out as a sentence and solved them in words, using *root* to mean the primary unknown number and *square* or *cube* for the powers of that root.

For example, al-Khwārizmī wrote that "one square, and ten roots of the same, amount to thirty-nine dirhems." By this, he indicated the mathematical relationship that we would write as follows:

$$x^2 + 10x = 39$$

He solved this riddle by the method we now call *completing the square.* If you have students in Algebra 2 or beyond, you might let them refresh their memory of that procedure and then try to explain the steps of al-Khwārizmī's solution:

> *The solution is this: you halve the number of the roots, which in the present instance yields five. This you multiply by itself; the product is twenty-five. Add this to thirty-nine; the sum is sixty-four. Now take the root of this, which is eight, and subtract from it half the number of the roots, which is five; the remainder is three. This is the root of the square which you sought for; the square itself is nine.*

Challenge your kids with the following secret number riddles, taken from Frederic Rosen's 1831 translation.[†] Elementary children may solve these puzzles by testing numbers until they find some that fit. Older students can practice setting up algebra equations, though they will want to use modern symbols, which are much easier to work with than al-Khwārizmī's words.

- ◆ I have divided ten into two parts. I have afterwards divided the one by the other, and the quotient was four. [answer22]

- ◆ I have divided ten into two parts, and multiplying one of these by the other, the result was twenty-one. [answer23]

- ◆ You divide ten into two parts: multiply the one by itself; it will be equal to the other taken eighty-one times. [answer24]

- ◆ I have divided ten into two parts; I have then multiplied each of them by itself, and when I had added the products together, the sum was fifty-eight dirhems. [answer25]

---

† *http://books.google.com/books?id=3bNDAAAAIAAJ*

♦ I have divided ten into two parts; and have divided the first by the second, and the second by the first, and the sum of the quotients is two dirhems and one-sixth. [answer26]

Now try writing some secret number puzzles of your own.

European Recovery

950–1500

The Europeans began to translate works from Arabic into Latin, and in the process they rediscovered mathematics. Fibonacci popularized the Hindu-Arabic numerals. The invention of the printing press allowed ideas to spread faster than ever before. Mathematics became a required course at the University of Paris. Men pondered the ideas of infinity, and the world stood poised on the brink of an intellectual revolution.

Mathematicians include Gerbert of Aurillac, Adelard of Bath, Gerard of Cremona, Leonardo Pisano Fibonacci, Nicole Oresme, Nicholas of Cusa, and Luca Pacioli.

Fibonacci's Story Problems

As the son of a merchant, Leonardo Fibonacci traveled around the Mediterranean world. When he returned to his hometown of Pisa, Italy, in 1200 CE, he brought back "new" ideas about math. He rediscovered concepts that had been lost to the Europeans since the fall of Rome. Even more important, Fibonacci brought to Europe the Hindu-Arabic numbering system and the notion of zero.

Fibonacci's book *Liber Abbaci* ("The Book of Calculation") contained a great many story problems, including the following:

♦ There are seven old men on the road to Rome. Each man has seven mules. Each mule carries seven sacks. In each sack are seven loaves. With each loaf are seven knives. Each knife is well protected in seven sheaths. Men, mules, sacks, loaves, knives, and sheaths … How many are there in all on the road to Rome? [answer27]

- A man entered the king's orchard through seven gates, each guarded by a royal soldier. While there, he gathered a certain number of apples. When the man left the orchard, the seven guards demanded bribes to let him out the gates. He gave the guard at the first gate half of the apples that he had picked plus one apple more. He gave the guard at the second gate half of his remaining apples plus one apple more. He did the same at each gate. When the man got home, he found he had only one apple left for himself. How many apples did he gather in the orchard? [answer28]

- Fibonacci's Rabbit Problem: Assume that baby rabbits take two months to mature. In the first month they are babies. The second month they are half-grown. In the third month they are adults that mate, producing babies of their own. Full-grown rabbits beget a new pair (male and female) of babies every month. No rabbits ever die. If you buy one pair of newborn baby rabbits on January 1, how many rabbits will you have at the end of the year? [answer29]

Mathematical Explosion

1450–1700

Mathematicians invented symbols and notation to help them write their ideas with precision. Logarithms allowed faster and more accurate calculation than ever before. All areas of mathematics grew rapidly as European mathematicians discovered the ideas of the Arabs and surpassed them. Descartes invented Cartesian coordinate geometry, which gave mathematicians a new tool for analyzing equations. Fermat and Pascal studied probability. Several people tried to understand the nature of motion and infinity, leading to the invention of calculus by Leibniz and Newton.

Last names, because there are so many: Tartaglia, Ferrari, Copernicus, Cardano, Recorde, Viète, Harriot, Kepler, Galileo, Napier, Briggs, Mersenne, Fermat, Oughtred, Descartes, Desargues, Cavalieri, Pascal, Huygens, Hooke, Newton, Leibniz, and the Bernoullis.

Napier's Chessboard Calculator

Baron John Napier lived in a castle near Edinburgh, Scotland, with a dozen children, evenly matched: six boys and six girls. Napier played with mathematics as a hobby. Unlike the professional mathematicians of his day, he did not consider long, complicated calculations a virtue. That is why he invented logarithms, which make it easier to multiply and divide large numbers and find their roots or powers.

Napier also invented the world's first binary computer, although he had never heard of the binary, or base two, number system. Using an ordinary chessboard and several counters (beans, pennies, or milk caps work well), he could add, subtract, multiply, and divide with numbers up to 255. Larger boards could handle even bigger numbers.

To make Napier's calculator yourself, label a chess or checkers board according to the following pattern:

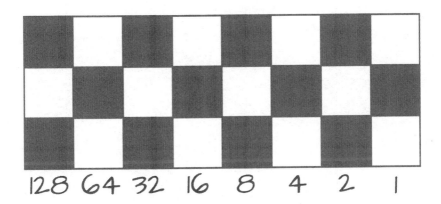

128   64   32   16   8   4   2   1

The columns of the board have become place-value columns for writing binary numbers:

$$2^0 = 1$$
$$2^1 = 2$$
$$2^2 = 4$$
$$2^3 = 8, \text{etc.}$$

How can you convert a decimal, or base ten, number to binary? Let's suppose you want to enter the number 103 on Napier's calculator:

- Find the largest power of two that is equal to or smaller than the number, and put a token in that column. (One penny on sixty-four.)

- Subtract that from your original number. (103 – 64 = 39)

- Next, find the largest power of two that is equal to or smaller than this difference. Put a token on that column. (One penny on thirty-two.)

- Subtract that from your number. (39 – 32 = 7)

- Continue this process until you run out of numbers. (Tokens on four, two, and one.)

- If you want to write the binary number, put a "1" for each token and a "0" for every empty space. (1100111)

The modern era also witnessed a growing worldwide
fascination with recreational mathematics.
Sam Loyd's *Eighth Book of Tan,* published in 1903,
included this set of "Magic Dice Cups."
Each cup is made from the same set of tangrams,
so how does the hole move around?

Now, can you think of a way to use Napier's calculating board to add or subtract numbers? [answer30]

Application and Abstraction

1700–Present

Since the discovery of calculus, mathematics has grown so much that no one can understand it all. Over this period, as physics and engineering became almost branches of mathematics, a growing distinction developed between "pure" and "applied" math.

People began to explore new worlds of imagination, such as non-Euclidean geometry, topology, and the "monster curves" we call fractals. Pure mathematicians prided themselves on studying theoretical ideas, and some disdained any math that was considered useful (though scientists kept finding practical ways to use those supposedly pure mathematical theories). Mathematicians tried to solidify the logical foundations of mathematics using set theory, and they continued to wrestle with ideas about infinity.

Some of the foremost names from this era: the Bernoullis, Euler, Agnesi, Lagrange, Laplace, Legendre, Monge, Gauss, Germain, Somerville, Fourier, Babbage, Lobachevski, Abel, Cauchy, Bolyai, Galois, Hamilton, Boole, Riemann, Dedekind, Möbius, Weierstrass, Kovalevskaya, Cantor, Poincaré, Hilbert, Noether, Whitehead, Russell, Hausdorff, Hardy, Ramanujan, Gödel, Turing, Erdös, Mandelbrot, Wiles, Perelman, Tao, and Mirzakhani.

Bertrand Russell's Barber

British earl, math professor, flamboyant philanderer, unsuccessful political candidate, anti-war protester, Nobel Laureate ... Few mathematicians have had as long and varied a career as the mathematical philosopher Bertrand Russell. Along with his friend, Alfred North Whitehead, Russell strove to put mathematics on a firm, logical foundation. Math, he claimed, was a branch of logic. So as he systematized logic, he was sure that math would fall in line. But the harder Russell worked to establish the foundations, the more the whole structure shook. The problem, he found, was at the deepest heart of math and logic: the notion of sets.

Even young children can understand sets. Sets are what the silverware comes in when they put it on the table, one set for each person. A set is any group of things that go together for some reason. The things that go together are called the members of that set.

"It seemed to me," Russell wrote, "that a class sometimes is, and sometimes is not, a member of itself. The class of teaspoons, for example, is not another teaspoon, but the class of things that are not teaspoons is one of the things that are not teaspoons."

Most sets are not members of themselves, of course. The set of all dogs is not itself a dog. But a few sets are members of themselves. The set of all abstract ideas is definitely an abstract idea. So far, everything made sense. But then Russell got into trouble. He began to wonder about the set of "all sets which are not members of themselves." Would that set be a member of itself, or not?

Or, to put the question into a story:

In a certain town, there lived a barber. Like most old codgers, this barber was a bit eccentric. You might even call him crotchety. One day, the barber declared, "I'm tired of trying to patch up botched shaving jobs done by amateurs and fools. From now on, I am going to shave all the inhabitants of this town that do not shave themselves—and nobody else." So that's what he did, and he lived grumpily ever after.

Except … Can you spot the problem? The paradox that Bertrand Russell found was this:

♦ Who shaves the barber? [answer31]

What do you think? Does the barber shave himself, or not? It seems like the barber can shave himself only if he does not shave himself. That's impossible, just like the set of "all sets which are not members of themselves" would be a member of itself only if it were not a member of itself. It's a contradiction. Russell realized that the whole idea of sets, which is the foundation of math and logic, is built on top of a contradiction. His whole structure was ready to tumble to the ground at any moment.

Mathematicians scrambled to find an answer to Russell's paradox. In the early twentieth century, German mathematician Ernst Zermelo published a set of *axioms* (rules to be accepted without having to be proved) about sets. This new axiomatic set theory, revised by later mathematicians, seemed to avoid the problem of Russell's paradox. But it was no longer the beautiful, simple theory that children intuitively understand.

Sometimes even the most abstract theory runs smack into the real world. In science, this happened to the notion of atoms as the smallest indivisible chunks of matter. Inside atoms, physicists discovered a new universe of smaller and smaller particles—except they are not exactly particles, because sometimes they act like waves. The beautiful, simple theory became the complex monster known as quantum mechanics. In ancient Greek mathematics, a similar thing happened when the idea that everything could be measured hit a brick wall with the discovery of irrational numbers.

So, in the first years of the twentieth century, mathematicians faced and conquered the crisis in set theory. They were not happy about accepting the new axioms, but the paradox forced them to abandon the earlier, simpler ideas. And like Bertrand Russell's barber, they could live with it, somewhat grumpily ever after.

Or could they?

In 1931, Kurt Gödel published a paper that again shook the foundations of math and logic. From that crisis, there could be no recovery. But that's another story....

"Can you do Addition?" the White Queen asked.
"What's one and one and one and one
and one and one and one and one and one and one?"

"I don't know," said Alice. "I lost count."

"She can't do Addition," the Red Queen interrupted.
"Can you do Subtraction? Take nine from eight."

"Nine from eight, I can't, you know,"
Alice replied very readily: "but—"

"She can't do Subtraction," said the White Queen.
"Can you do Division?
Divide a loaf by a knife.
What's the answer to that?"

—Lewis Carroll

Let's Get Practical

Weaving It All Together

WITH SO MANY CREATIVE OPTIONS for playing with mathematical ideas, sometimes I feel overwhelmed. It seems easier to shove a workbook across the table and tell my daughter, "Do two pages." Someone else has made all the decisions, so I don't even have to think.

Creative mathematical adventures require an investment of energy and time, but some days I don't have energy for anything beyond mere survival. We move to a new house, or we have another baby, or I agree to start a 4-H club and find out it is more work than I thought. Life gets hectic. I feel too rushed to sit down and read math storybooks or play games. Relying on the book is my easy way out.

But if I do it too often—if that is my children's primary experience of mathematics—my kids won't learn to appreciate the mental play aspect of the subject.

This is especially important for anyone working with a discouraged child or a child who is afraid of math. When children are forced to endure repetitive busywork or to rush through topics they do not understand, they learn to hate math. Their brains clam up in self-defense: they go into subsistence mode, taking in only enough to make it through today's lesson, refusing to care about long-term understanding. Why care about the impossible? It would hurt too much. One way to help a discouraged child is to put away the workbook. Try something different, fun, and challenging—such as the math doodling explorations in Anna Weltman's *This Is Not a Math Book.*

In other families, it is not the child but the parents themselves who are afraid of math, which can make the idea of stepping away from the crutch of a textbook program seem impossible. If that describes you, take heart: it is possible to learn math right alongside your child. The chance to revisit and appreciate the subjects I hated in school is one of my favorite side-effects of raising children. Begin your mathematical re-education with a book that explains math in normal English, such as *Dr. Wright's Kitchen Table Math Series* by Chris Wright or *Common Core Math for Parents for Dummies* by Christopher Danielson.

One Week of Real Mathematics

How does "math the mathematician's way" work in real life? It's not as complicated as you might think. I'm not trying to write my own math curriculum. I'm just feeding my children's curiosity about mathematical ideas. We do a little at a time, picking a topic and playing around until we are tired of it. Then we move on to something new. Variety makes for a balanced math diet.

Here is a sample of what one week's worth of math playtime might look like, using many of the ideas discussed in this book:

Monday

- ◆ Read a library book about a mathematician or a topic from math history.

- ◆ Or walk around your neighborhood. See how much math you can find: numbers, shapes, patterns, fractal growth, and symmetry. Take pictures, and post the best ones online for your friends to enjoy.

Tuesday

♦ Play with manipulatives. You might try Pattern Block Mastermind: "I made a secret pattern with three blocks in a row. Can you guess what it is?"

♦ Or measure the living room and draw a floor plan on graph paper. Cut out scale models of the furniture. How would you like to rearrange the room?

Wednesday

♦ Take turns making up oral story problems. Write down your children's favorites to save for their school journals or portfolios.

♦ Or play a card game to practice math facts.

Thursday

♦ Use your drafting tools to draw geometric designs. Color in your favorite design to display on the refrigerator.

♦ Or work KenKen puzzles for arithmetic practice. You can sign up for the free KenKen teachers' program to receive new puzzles every week at KenkenPuzzle.com.

Friday

♦ Browse your favorite math websites for activity ideas. For a treasure trove of online math, see the appendix "Math Resources on the Internet" (page 219).

♦ Or have "Children's Choice" of any mathematical book or game.

My primary goal in these exercises is to provide as many opportunities as I can for my children to discover and enjoy the multitude of interconnected ideas called mathematics. Their understanding will build in an ever-growing spiral as we talk together about math concepts, create physical models, draw pictures, and tell each other stories.

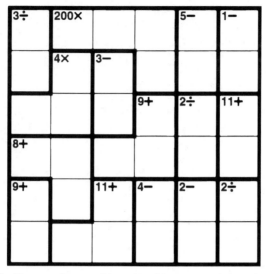

KenKen puzzles provide enjoyable cross-training play, blending arithmetic practice with logical reasoning. Each row and each column contain the numbers one through six. The numbers within each outlined shape must add, subtract, multiply, or divide to make the number shown.

What About Workbooks?

With all this to do, do your children need a textbook? Maybe, or maybe not. Like everything in parenting, it depends on your family.

A too-early emphasis on formal, written arithmetic can lead young children to develop a rules-and-recipes mindset. Remember, it's not the written symbols that make math—it's the way we notice and think about numbers, shapes, and patterns in the world around us.

If your kids ask for a workbook, like my girls who enjoyed playing school, then buy something inexpensive. I prefer the *Miquon Math* series by Lore Rasmussen, but department store workbooks are fine, or download some practice pages from a worksheet generator website. Explain the notation and show your children how to model the numbers with blocks or other manipulatives, but don't force them to do any of the pages. Given such freedom, they may surprise you by begging to learn long division, as one of my daughters did when she was eight. I told her she was too young for that, which made her even more determined to master the concept.

If your school-age children learn math with a textbook, whether in a classroom or homeschooling, don't let them fall into the trap of believing that calculations are the heart of math. Keep thinking like a mathematician—looking for the patterns, connections, and reasons behind the book's rules—and be sure to reserve time for supplemental games and activities. For instance, many families enjoy setting aside Friday's math homework time to read aloud living books or as a math game play date.

For families who choose homeschooling: many parents suffer from a nagging suspicion that we will miss something if we take an off-the-beaten-path approach to math. Some vital topic we failed to teach will destroy our children's future. If that describes you, then make the transition to more formal math lessons in upper elementary school sometime between third and fifth grade. With my older children, I introduced traditional arithmetic methods using an outdated fourth-grade book I picked up cheap at a local public school's used book sale, but today's parents have the advantage of the Internet. Try Geoff Krall's Problem-Based Curriculum website for your older students. Or explore the curriculum maps at the Nrich Enriching Mathematics website. (A *curriculum map* is a grade-level list of math projects, games, and lessons, arranged to flow in a natural progression.)[†]

As a math professor who trains teachers, John Golden recognizes the danger of relying on textbooks. He warns, "The toughest thing for a homeschooler is the same as for a school teacher—shifting from a weak tea vision of math being grinding calculations to a rich frothy mug of math as an active way of thinking."

The advantage of a prepared math program is security, knowing that the workbook or video lessons will remind us of topics that we might otherwise forget to teach our kids. But this security comes at a heavy price. Too often, a math curriculum leads parents and teachers to rely on "talking at" our children. It is easy for adults to believe that we can explain math to our children. If they would just listen to us, we imagine, we could tell them everything they need to know. But learning never works like that. It didn't work that way for us when we were kids, and it won't work that way for our children. Even with the best of intentions, adult talk often comes through like the distorted "Blah, blah, blah" of the parents in

†   *http://emergentmath.com/my-problem-based-curriculum-maps (grades 3 and up)*
http://nrich.maths.org/8935 (primary levels)
http://nrich.maths.org/8517 (secondary levels)

a Charlie Brown cartoon.

Also, elementary textbooks specialize in repetition, which easily degenerates into busywork that kills the "Aha!" thrill of solving problems. In second through eighth grades, 50–80% of each year's book reviews what the children did the year before. It does not take eight years to learn the basics of arithmetic when we work one-on-one. Whatever math program you choose, remember that you are the master. The textbook is your servant. Your goal is not to finish the book, but to learn the concepts. So you don't have to follow the curriculum exactly, to work every question on a worksheet or do every activity in a section. You can visit the chapters out of order or skip topics entirely, if you want. Feel free to use no more than your child needs.

Buddy Math to the Rescue

My children dislike workbook arithmetic when forced to do it on their own. Their minds wander, and it takes them half an hour to work one math problem. Nagging doesn't help, because as soon as my back is turned, they end up staring out the window again. Rather than turn into the textbook police, I developed the habit of doing "buddy math." My daughter and I take turns working the problems in her workbook—mine, hers, mine, hers, and so on down the page.

This approach requires a bit of patience. My children are easily distracted, heading down every conversational rabbit trail they can find. Still, I believe that three or four problems well-explained make for better practice than a whole page of dawdling and foot-dragging. It surprises me how much fun a workbook can be when we do it sitting together on the couch. One day, my daughter insisted on weaving the math problems together as an ongoing story. I was not allowed to go to the next one until she had introduced it into her narrative.

We limit our sessions to ten minutes or less per grade level. For example, a fourth-grade student would not work more than forty minutes. We often split that into twenty minutes of workbook time and twenty minutes of more playful activities. I let my daughter choose whether to take her turn first or second and whether to skip around the page, which allows her to avoid the problems that might otherwise bring her to tears. We work each problem out loud, explaining how we got the answer and checking each other as we go, which helps both of us build our mental math skills.

Because my daughter has to process her thoughts in order to explain how she worked the problem, buddy math fixes the concepts firmly in her mind. When it's my turn to do a problem, I model the type of explanation I want to hear from her. I work slowly, with frequent pauses, hoping to give her mind time to skip ahead and predict my next move. Sometimes she will jump in and finish a problem for me.

If I don't understand what she's doing, I ask her to explain again. Then I listen attentively. She almost never thinks the way I do, but that doesn't mean she's wrong. Many people believe math must always be done by the book's method, but there are many valid ways to approach almost any problem. All of my children have done math in ways I would never have imagined, and I learned a lot from trying to figure out their point of view.

Our discussion is the important thing. The answers are an almost insignificant byproduct. Sometimes we don't even bother to work out the final calculation because what intrigues us is the web of ideas: how can we think our way through this problem? What other problems are related, and how do they help us understand this one? Or can this problem help us understand others? What could we do if we've never seen a problem like this before? Why does the formula work? What is the easiest or most efficient way to manipulate the numbers—and does this help us see more of the patterns and connections within our number system? Is there another way to approach this problem? How many different ways can we think of? Which approach do we prefer?

When my daughter gets stuck on a problem, I try not to give away the answer. Instead, we investigate together how the math works and why. We may try a similar but easier problem to show the principles, or I might draw a picture or use manipulatives to act the problem out. Or if she is truly struggling—especially if I notice her fighting back tears—I may choose to give up. When an idea doesn't click after several tries, we switch to something different. By the time we come back to the hard topic another day, she often surprises me by figuring it out on her own.

Robin Padron advocates a similar parental-involvement approach she calls Full-Contact math in her book *How to Homeschool Math—Even If You Hate Fractions.* "Story time is precious, a time when they have our undivided attention. Even if just for a few minutes, you, they, and the book are all that matters," she writes. "But with math, it's a whole different story. Maybe we start out early with lots of interaction, counting yellow duckies and the like, but pretty soon it is: 'Take these exercises, go off into solitary confinement and do them. Then come back, and I'll tell you what you did wrong' ... [In contrast,] Full-Contact math involves you, the parent, being involved in each and every little bit of math you expect your kids to do, which is a fundamental shift in the way most of us think about teaching our kids math."

Buddy math is not only for elementary children. My daughter and I still work this way in high school algebra. My older kids did a similar thing in our co-op geometry class, going around the table and taking turns explaining the key steps in each proof.

Some people worry that sharing math lessons will make their children dependent or keep them from learning to work on their own. I find that my kids have a natural desire to be independent. They do learn to work by themselves, on their own interests. But life is easier for all of us if they get a little help on the things they don't enjoy. This is true for everyone, isn't it? I, too, find it easier to do an unpleasant task (such as exercising or cleaning house) when I work with a partner.

The Importance of Mental Math

Whether you work with a math curriculum or take a less-traditional route, do not be satisfied with mere pencil-and-paper competence. Instead, build your children's mental math skills, because mental calculation forces a child to understand arithmetic at a much deeper level than is required by traditional pencil-and-paper methods. The techniques that let us work with numbers in our heads reflect the fundamental properties of arithmetic:

♦ We can take numbers apart and put them together in different ways.

$$57 = 55 + 2$$
$$\text{or } 50 + 7$$
$$\text{or } 40 + 17 \text{ or...}$$

♦ We can rearrange a calculation to make it easier.

$$1 + 2 + 3 + 4 + 5$$
$$= (1 + 4) + (2 + 3) + 5$$
$$= 5 + 5 + 5 = 15$$

♦ We can do a calculation in parts, and then put the parts back together at the end.

$$6 \times 23$$
$$= (6 \times 20) + (6 \times 3)$$
$$= 120 + 18 = 138$$

Mathematicians call the principle that we can take numbers apart and put them together in different ways the *associative property*. That we can rearrange a calculation to make it easier is the *commutative property*. The mighty ability to do a calculation in parts and then put the parts back together at the end is called the *distributive property*. Your textbook may explain these properties in technical terms, but don't be intimidated by the jargon. These are just common-sense rules for playing with numbers.

These principles are also fundamental to algebra, which explains why flexibility and confidence in mental math is one of the best predictors of success in high school math and beyond.

Look for opportunities for your children to practice mental calculation skills. If you use a textbook, try reading the problems aloud, letting the child answer without writing anything. Oral work has another advantage: young children need not be limited by their still-developing fine motor skills. My sons, in particular, were able to advance through math topics orally that they would never have had the patience to write down. As students progress to more difficult problems, they may wish to have scratch paper or a whiteboard and colorful markers handy. Even then, however, we do as much work as we can in our heads.

As veteran teacher Ruth Beechick wrote, "If you stay with meaningful mental arithmetic longer, you will find that your child, if she is average, can do problems much more advanced than the level listed for her grade. You will find that she likes arithmetic more. And when she does get to abstractions, she will understand them better."

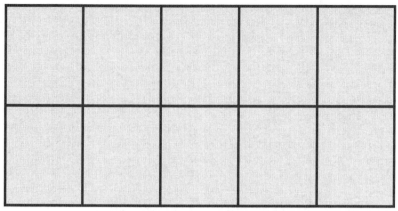

You can cut a 4×8-foot sheet of glossy white
paneling from the lumber store to make ten lap-size
whiteboards for use with dry-erase markers.

Mastering the Math Facts

Math facts are the basic relationships between one-digit numbers, such as
3 + 4 = 7 and 5 × 8 = 40. Many parents stress out over teaching the math
facts, but children do not have to memorize long lists of number facts to
be great at math. And memory work is no panacea: even children who can
recite the times tables flawlessly may be reduced to counting on fingers in
the middle of a long division problem or have no clue how to approach a
word problem.

There is only one thing our children must learn: how to use whatever
number facts they do remember to figure out the answers they forget.
And the best way to learn this is the mathematician's way—by playing
with numbers. The traditional elementary-level emphasis on drilling math
facts encourages rote memory and punishes mistakes, but number play
strengthens relational thinking and celebrates creativity.

Let's try a few examples.

Addition: 6 + 8 = ?

The most important math facts for children to learn for addition and subtraction are the doubles and the combinations that make ten. They can
find all the other facts from these.

For instance, how might children think through an addition puzzle such as 6 + 8? If we try to count on our fingers, we'll probably lose track, so how can we make it easier? When we look at six beads and eight beads on a rekenrek, it's easy to see a pair of fives. That leads to our first simplified calculation.

$$6 + 8$$
$$= 5 + 5 + 1 + 3$$
$$= 10 + 4$$

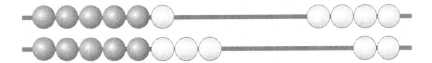

Addition on a rekenrek. We push the beads we aren't
using over to the right-hand edge, out of the way.

What other patterns might we find? Oh, look, it's the same as double-six plus two extra:

$$6 + 8$$
$$= 6 + 6 + 2$$

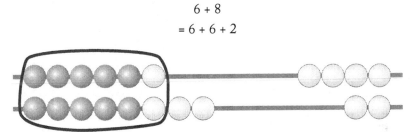

Doubles make addition easier.

We could imagine moving one bead from the eight row up to join the six, making double-seven:

$$6 + 8$$
$$= 7 + 7$$

If we slide a lower bead over to the right and replace it by sliding in
a bead on the top row, the total number of beads remains the same.

Or move two beads from the six row down to join the eight, making a ten:

$$6 + 8$$
$$= 4 + 10$$

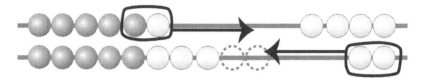

If we slide two beads away from the top number and replace them with two on the bottom, we still have the same number of beads.

This sort of number play works far beyond the range of traditional math facts. If the calculation was 36 + 48, children who are comfortable manipulating numbers might see 3 + 4 tens and 6 + 8 ones, making the answer seventy-fourteen, a funny name for eighty-four. Or they might notice that forty-eight is almost fifty and imagine moving a couple pieces from the other pile to make the calculation easier. Or move four pieces over to the thirty-six, making double forty plus four extra pieces.

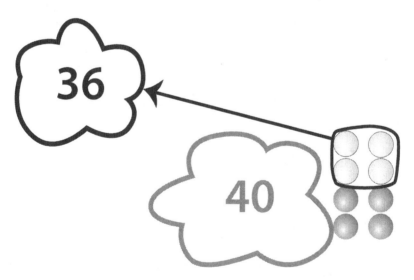

With larger numbers, we don't try to visualize all the individual beads. Imagine two piles of beads, which we can shift around as needed. 36 + 48 = 40 + 40 + 4.

Subtraction: 17 – 9 = ?

Subtraction is backward addition, so we don't need to memorize a list of subtraction facts. If your children know addition, then for subtraction they can think, "How many would I add?"

So how might children think through a subtraction puzzle such as 17 – 9? If we start with nine beads, how many more do we need in order to have seventeen? Adding one gets us up to ten, and then we need seven more beads to get the rest of the way to seventeen:

$$17 - 9$$
$$= 1 + 7$$

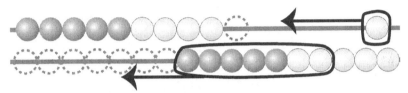

How many of the extra beads do we need
to make a total of seventeen?

Or think about subtraction as taking stuff away, so we would start with seventeen and remove nine. But don't count—we have to use logic. If only it was 17 – 10, that would be easy, because we could just get rid of ten beads and keep the seven. But we were only supposed to remove nine, so we took away too much. We'll have to put one bead back.

$$17 - 9$$
$$= 17 - 10 + 1$$
$$= 7 + 1$$

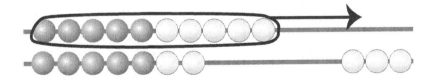

It's easy to take away ten.

Or we could take away a little at a time, in easy chunks. We might take away seven beads, so we'll have ten left. Then we still need to take away two more:

$$17 - 9$$
$$= 17 - 7 - 2$$
$$= 10 - 2$$

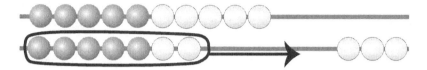

It's easy to take away seven.

Or we could think about doubles: eighteen is double-nine, so it would be easy to take one of the nines away. There would be nine beads left. But we're starting with one less than eighteen, which means we'll end up with one less than nine:

$$17 - 9$$
$$= 18 - 9 - 1$$
$$= 9 - 1$$

Eighteen is double nine, so 18 − 9 would be easy.

Or ... Can you think of any other ways to do it?

Multiplication: 8 × 7 = ?

For multiplication and division, if children learn the doubles and the square numbers, they can reason out everything else from those. (A *square number* is the answer when you multiply a number times itself, the columns and rows in an actual square of blocks: two rows of two, three rows of three, etc.) Once kids master the doubles and squares, show them how to split the difficult numbers up into easier ones.

Let's give it a try: how many ways might children think their way through the calculation 8 × 7?

When we double a number, we get twice as much as we had at first. If we double it again, that will give us four times our original number. If we double it a third time, then we get double-four (which is eight) times as much as the number we started with. Times two is double, times four is double-double, and times eight is double-double-double.

So counting up eight sevens looks like this:

$$8 \times 7$$
$$= \text{double (double (double 7))}$$
$$= \text{double (double 14)}$$
$$= \text{double 28}$$
$$= \text{forty-sixteen}$$
$$= 56$$

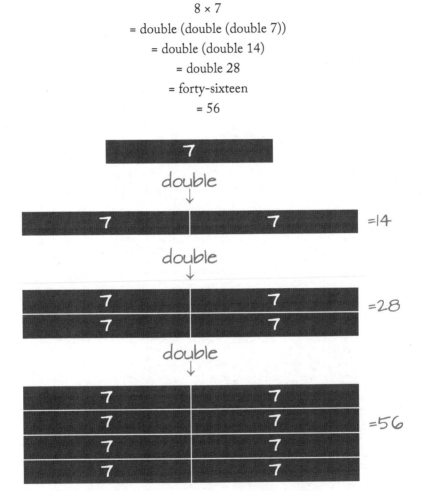

We can double larger numbers in chunks.
Double the tens, double the ones, and then
add them together to get our answer.
Fourteen is one ten and four extra pieces,
so doubling it will make two tens and eight extras.

Or use a square number: think of seven sevens and one more seven.

$$8 \times 7 = (7 \times 7) + 7$$
$$= 49 + 7$$
$$= 49 + 1 + 6$$
$$= 50 + 6$$

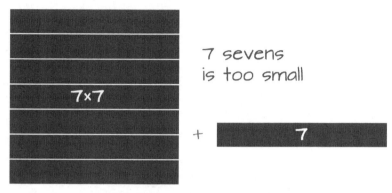

7 sevens
is too small

When we know the square numbers,
we can use them to find related number facts.

Or eight eights minus one of the eights:

$$8 \times 7 = (8 \times 8) - 8$$
$$= 64 - 8 = 64 - 4 - 4$$
$$= 60 - 4$$

We can use any
nearby number
fact we happen
to remember
and then
adjust it to get
the answer
we need.

Or use the distributive property to do the calculation in smaller chunks. Think of five eights and two more eights. Two eights is a double, and five eights is easy because it's exactly half of ten eights:

$$8 \times 7 = (8 \times 5) + (8 \times 2)$$
$$= (\tfrac{1}{2} \text{ of } 80) + 16$$
$$= 40 + 16$$

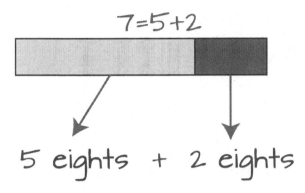

Splitting a number into smaller pieces will
often make a calculation easier.

Division: 42 ÷ 6 = ?

In the same way that subtraction is the inverse of addition, division is the mirror image of multiplication. So we don't need to memorize a separate list of division facts. Just think, "How many would I multiply?"

Let's test that approach on the calculation 42 ÷ 6. How might children think it through? Six times *what* makes forty-two?

$$42 \div 6 = ? \text{ means:}$$
$$42 = 6 \times ?$$

Well, six squared is thirty-six, which isn't quite big enough. Adding one more six makes thirty-twelve, the same as forty-two.

Think:
$$42 = 36 + 6$$
$$= (6 \times 6) + (1 \times 6)$$
So:
$$42 \div 6 = 6 + 1$$

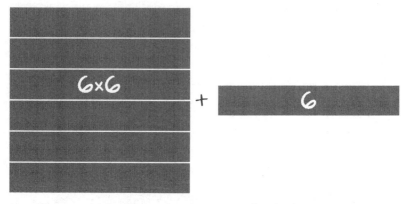

When we think of division as the inverse of multiplication, we can use the square numbers and other times-table facts to figure it out.

Or we could use the distributive property to split forty-two into smaller chunks that we know how to divide. Forty-two is thirty and twelve more, which is five sixes and two more sixes:

Think:

$$42 = 30 + 12$$
$$= (5 \times 6) + (2 \times 6)$$

So:

$$42 \div 6 = 5 + 2$$

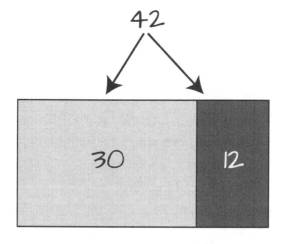

Splitting a number into smaller pieces will often make a calculation easier.

Or we could count up how many sixes there are by doubling. Two sixes make twelve. Doubling that gives us four sixes = two twelves = twenty-four. Doubling one more time will make eight sixes = two twenty-fours = forty-eight. Oops! That's too big, so we need to take back one of the sixes.

Think:

$$2 \times [2 \times (2 \times 6)]$$
$$= 48 = 8 \times 6$$
$$48 - 6 = 42$$

So:

$$42 \div 6 = 8 - 1$$

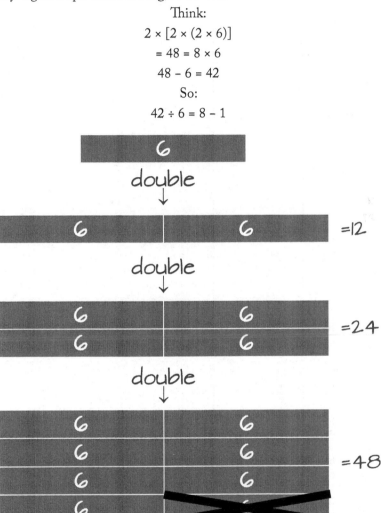

We can even use doubling to figure out a division problem.

Did you find the written-out calculations hard to follow? Don't force your children to write down their mental math. It looks dreary when I write the calculations out step by step, but with regular practice, this sort of thinking becomes second nature.

For older students, Fawn Nguyen has posted more than two dozen mental math prompts at her Math Talks site, with samples of her middle school students' responses. Nguyen encourages discussion: "I'm not worried about the correct answer right now," she tells her students. "I'm just interested in how you thought about the problem. Your sharing of how you arrived at the incorrect answer is really important—I think we learn a lot from our mistakes, and as you can see, you weren't the only one who thought about it that way."[†]

Mental Math Do's and Don'ts

- ♦ Don't just count. Limit straight counting to a few steps, so you don't lose track. That means you may work 39 + 2 by counting, but not 39 + 7.

- ♦ When you do count, always start at the bigger number, so you have fewer steps.

- ♦ Do break numbers apart. Work with the easier parts first.

- ♦ Do use logic to rearrange your numbers and make your calculation easier. For instance, to find 39 + 7 you can imagine moving one piece from the seven to the big pile: 39 + 7 is the same as 40 + 6.

- ♦ Don't try to keep track of "borrowing" or "carrying" numbers while you work.

- ♦ Do use funny numbers such as seventy-fourteen as an intermediate step. If you remember that 9 + 7 = 16, then you might think of 39 + 7 as thirty-sixteen.

- ♦ Do (usually) start from the left and work the bigger place-value parts of your calculation first.

- ♦ Do feel free to work the place-value columns out of order, if that makes the calculation easier.

- ♦ Don't try to memorize everything.

- ♦ Do memorize a few basic facts (such as the pairs of numbers that make ten) that you can use to figure out other things.

† _http://www.mathtalks.net_

- Don't try to use the same trick on every calculation.

- Do be creative, looking for new ways to figure things out.

- Do use fingers, manipulatives, or marks on paper to keep track of information while you work, especially with longer, multistep calculations.

- Do allow your children plenty of time to think. Practice patience.

- Don't worry if your children stare blankly into space. That's what "thinking hard" looks like. Don't break their concentration.

Your children will learn the number facts through repeated use. My goal is the same as those who emphasize memory drill: fluency in using math to solve problems. But my children and I spend the early- to mid-elementary years playing games that focus on mental math, such as the games in my *Math You Can Play* series of books. We put off memorization as long as possible, so that it becomes a mopping-up operation. At that point, we work on committing to memory the few remaining facts that my children found most confusing.

No matter where you stand in the continuum between textbook instruction and total unschooling, timed drill and laid-back play, the important question remains the same. What is your mathematical world-view? Are you showing your children techniques for getting right answers, or are you weaving a web of interrelated ideas? How you answer that question will guide your response to many of the stumbling blocks you meet along your educational journey.

Special Cases

In the following chapter, we'll look at several frequently asked questions about kids and math. In my answers, I assume you are working with children of normal intelligence, facing the mental strengths and weaknesses that are common to us all. The human brain is not designed for working with abstraction, so most people find math difficult.

But some children face additional hardship because their minds are unable to process numbers and related concepts. If you suspect one or more of your children may struggle with a learning disability, please have them tested and get advice from someone who can help you learn to deal with their special circumstances.

Auditory or vision problems, undiagnosed food allergies, and a family crisis or other emotional strain may also affect a child's concentration. Sometimes, the best way to help your children learn math is to let it go and deal with other issues first.

I'll let you in on a secret about teaching: there is no place in the world where it rolls along smoothly without problems. Only in articles and books can that happen.
—Dr. Ruth Beechick

Struggling with Math

LEARNING MATH IS AN ADVENTURE into the unknown. The ideas we adults take for granted are a wild, unexplored country to our children. Like any traveler in a strange land, they will stumble over rocky places and meet with unexpected detours. Whenever I visit a parenting forum, I feel compassion for the families who are struggling with math. No other school subject elicits such depths of frustration and despair:

- ♦ I've explained until I'm hoarse, and she still doesn't get it. Help!! I want to pull my hair out.

- ♦ My child is not a mathy person at all. Now he's convinced that he's "dumb."

- ♦ She says she can't do it. She says she hates math. She says she can't think. She hits her head and pounds her fists in frustration. I am so tired of fighting over math Every. Single. Day.

- ♦ The problem is not him … It's me. I am a failure at math.

- ♦ I am sooooo struggling to teach my daughter math. Please, does anybody else deal with this? I will try anything!

Solving the problems of math education is not easy. Situations have built up over years, so they will take time to resolve. But children are resilient, so improvement may not take as long as you fear. No matter how much your family has struggled, there is hope. If children can get over the "I'm no good at math" mental block, they can learn all of elementary arithmetic in one school year of determined study using a resource such as Herb Gross's Math as a Second Language webpages.[†]

The following questions are based on actual forum discussions, though I've changed the details, removing anything that might identify the families involved. The questions cover a wide range of common frustrations that will resonate with anyone who has tried to explain an abstract idea to a confused child. Some questions apply specifically to homeschool math, yet non-homeschooling families can use the resources I recommend to supplement their children's schoolwork or to keep skills sharp over the summer.

Lifelong Learning for Parents

Teaching Myself First

> *I'm so tired of being ignorant about math. I can memorize rules and do calculations, but if I miss a step the numbers make no sense at all, and I can't spot what went wrong. Another struggle I have is keeping everything organized in my mind. When I learn a new concept or strategy, I easily forget it. My son is only a toddler now, but as he grows up, I don't want to burden him with my own failures. Where should I start?*

As a first step, convince yourself that math is interesting enough to learn on its own merits, because parental guilt will only carry you so far. Start with Steven Strogatz's "Elements of Math" series from *The New York Times,* or pick up his book *The Joy of x.*[‡]

As a next step, reassure yourself that elementary math is hard to understand, so it's not strange that you get confused or don't know how to explain a topic. Get Liping Ma's *Knowing and Teaching Elementary*

---

† *https://www.scribd.com/doc/14389275/And-Rithmetic-by-Daniel-Greenberg*
http://www.lovemath.org/id10.html
http://www.lovemath.org/id15.html
‡ *http://topics.nytimes.com/top/opinion/series/steven_strogatz_on_the_elements_of_math/index.html*

Mathematics from the library or order a used copy of the first edition. Ma examines what it means to understand math and to clearly explain it to others. Don't rush through the book as if it were a novel. There are four open-ended questions, each at the beginning of a chapter, after which several possible answers are analyzed. When you read one of these questions, close the book. Think about how you would answer it yourself. Write out a few notes, explaining your thoughts as clearly as you can. Only then, after you have decided what you would have said, read the rest of that section. Don't worry if you can't understand everything in the book. Come back to it again in a couple of years. You'll be surprised how much more you learn.

To build up your own understanding of elementary arithmetic, the *Kitchen Table Math* book series by Chris Wright offers explanations and activities you can try with your son.[†]

If you want more detailed guidance in understanding and explaining each stage of elementary mathematics, you can pick up a textbook designed for teachers in training. I like the Parker & Baldridge *Elementary Mathematics for Teachers* books and the *Teaching Student-Centered Mathematics: Developmentally Appropriate Instruction* series. The two series are completely different, but they complement each other well. Check out the sample chapters from the publishers' websites to see which one you prefer.[‡]

As you learn, focus on how the math concepts relate to each other. Then the more you learn, the easier you will find it to connect things in your mind and to grasp new ideas. You might want to keep a math journal about the things you are learning. When you write something down, that helps you remember it, even if you never look back at the journal. But if your mind goes blank and you think, "I know I studied that," the journal gives you a quick way to review. Make it even easier to flip back through by writing the topic you are studying in the top margin of each page. When you run into a new vocabulary word, draw a Frayer model chart and fill in all the sections. And if you read something that's particularly helpful, you may want to turn to the back page of your journal and start a

---

† *http://www.drwrightskitchentablemath.com/books.html*

‡ *http://iremt.webfactional.com/SA/index.php/elementary-mathematics-for-teachers*
http://www.sefton-ash.com/index.php/elementary-geometry-for-teachers
http://www.pearsonhighered.com/educator/product/Teaching-StudentCentered-Mathematics-Developmentally-Appropriate-Instruction-for-Grades-PreK2-Volume-I/9780132824828.page

quick-reference section.

Find a fellow-learner to encourage you on your journey. Bouncing ideas off a friend is a great way to learn. You might want to join the parents and teachers who are learning math together at the Living Math Forum.[†]

And here is the most important piece of advice I can offer. Your slogan must be the one used by the Chinese teachers Liping Ma interviewed: "Know how, and also know why." Always ask why the rules you learn in math work. Don't stop asking until you find someone who can explain it in a way that makes sense to you.

When you struggle with a concept and conquer it, it will make you free. You don't have to be afraid of it anymore.

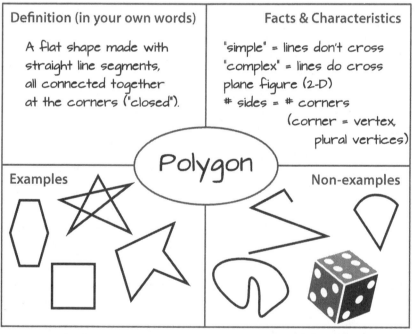

The Frayer model provides a way to organize information about a new vocabulary word or math concept.

† *https://groups.yahoo.com/neo/groups/LivingMathForum/info*

Primary Level Problems

Trouble with Worksheets

> *Worksheet problems make my daughter's brain freeze. Even simple things such as 2 + ___ = 2 confuse her. What can I do?*

Can your daughter do math if you put away the worksheet and ask her a real-life problem: "I have a lunch sack. I put two cookies into the sack, and then I give it to you. When you look into the sack, you see two cookies there. Can you tell me what was in the sack at the beginning, before I put my cookies in?"

Or can she solve problems when the answer isn't zero? Could she figure out how many you started with if she saw four cookies when she looked in the sack? The idea of having a number for "nothing" can seem strange to young children.

Or can your daughter think mathematically, without calculations? Try watching Christopher Danielson's video "One is one … or is it?" together, and then see how many different examples of "one" she can find around the house.[†]

Many children at this age have a hard time with abstract number math—then their brains will grow up, and they'll be able to do it. Development varies from one child to another. When I do worksheets with young children, I turn each equation into a little story. Sometimes we use blocks or other manipulatives to count on, but often the mental picture of a story is enough. Having something solid to imagine helps the child reason out the relationship between the numbers and symbols.

He Won't Stop Finger-Counting

> *My oldest son has somehow developed the horrid habit of counting on his fingers. We worked on the math facts all summer. He knows the answers in simple form, such as 9 + 4, but if it's in a bigger problem like 249 + 54, he counts up to add or counts down to subtract, all using fingers. My younger children have no problem with mental math, but he can't seem to get it. Are there any tips or tricks to stop this?*

† *https://youtu.be/EtclcWGG7WQ*

Counting on fingers is not a horrid habit, it is a crutch. Please think for a moment about the purpose of crutches. The blasted things are an uncomfortable nuisance, but there are times when you can't get anywhere without them. And if you need them, it does you no good for a friend to insist you should crawl along on your own. That is how your son feels right now about his fingers. He is struggling with something his younger siblings find easy, and he can tell that you are frustrated. His confidence is broken, in a cast, and needs time for healing. So he falls back on what he knows he can do, counting up the answer.

Think positive: this means he still believes that math ought to make sense—that to understand what he is doing is more important than to guess at an answer. You want him to value sense-making, because otherwise he will try to memorize his way through middle school and high school math. That is the road to disaster.

What you describe is called the problem of transfer, and it is one of the huge, unsolved problems of education. We can train someone to do a simple, limited task such as answering flash cards. But how do we get that knowledge to sink in, to become part of the mind, so they can use it in all sorts of different situations? No one has figured that out. There is no easy solution. It requires patience, and providing a variety of experiences, and patience, and pointing out connections, and asking the student to think of connections, and lots more patience.

It might help to do fewer math problems in a day, so you can take time to work more deeply on each one. Talk together about the different ways you might solve it. Make it a challenge: "Can we think of three different ways to do it?" In math, there is never just one way to get a solution. Thinking about alternatives will help your son develop that transfer of skills.

Or pick up some workbooks that target mental math methods. The *Mental Math* workbook series by Jack Hope and Barbara and Robert Reys will help him master the techniques your younger kids learned without effort. It may still take him longer to do a calculation than what you are used to with the other children, but these books will give him a boost in recognizing the types of mental tools he can use.

Jumping into mental math is hard for an older child who wasn't taught that way. I believe it's a battle worth fighting, because those mental math

Math that captures a child's imagination can make the more tedious work seem bearable. In the 1920s, mathematician David Hilbert created an interesting story about an imaginary grand hotel with an infinite number of rooms.

http://www.hotel-infinity.com

techniques build understanding of the fundamental properties of numbers. But the main goal is for him to recognize his options and build flexibility, not to do each calculation as fast as possible. And be sure he no longer needs those crutches before you try to take them away.

Running Out of Things to Try

I can't find a home school math program my son likes. We've tried Singapore Math, Right Start, Saxon, and Math Mammoth. We subscribed to a month of IXL Math to keep him in practice, but he hates that, too. I know I shouldn't have changed so many times, but this was our first year of homeschooling, and I was trying to please him. Do you think Life of Fred might work?

You've tried all those math programs in one year? Many people recommend that new homeschoolers take a few months off to "detox" from the classroom setting, to relax and enjoy the freedom of making their own choices. But your son might want a few months to detox from his homeschool experience.

I suggest you set aside all those books and focus on games and informal math. Try to avoid schoolish lessons until your son starts to enjoy learning for its own sake. The Internet offers an abundance of creative math ideas.

For example, download the Wuzzit Trouble app to play with, but don't make it a homework assignment. Or let him choose one of the activities at Gordon Hamilton's Math Pickle website and explore it for a day or a week or as long as it remains interesting.[†] Browse through the Primary Level 1 or Level 2 puzzles and games at the Nrich Mathematics website for more ideas.[‡] Or take a mental trip to infinity by playing with fractals. Cynthia Lanius's online Fractals Unit for Elementary and Middle School Students offers a child-friendly starting point.[§]

If you worry that your son needs to keep practicing traditional arithmetic during his break, try making him a series of Daily Four pages:

- ◆ Fold a sheet of plain paper in half both ways, making four quarter sections.

- ◆ Write one math problem in each part. Choose them from any of your math books.

- ◆ Make sure each problem is different—one addition, one fractions, one multiplication, or whatever—and that none of them are hard enough to cause frustration.

- ◆ Don't worry about an answer sheet. Show him how to use a calculator to check his work.

You can make up a whole week's worth of these problem sheets at once, with a balanced mix of problems for each day. Your son won't feel overwhelmed, but you'll know he's reviewing his number skills.

Or download some of the Corbettmaths 5-a-Day practice sheets for him. Some problems may seem too easy while others require concepts he hasn't studied yet. Easy review won't hurt anything, but do let him skip the problems that feel too hard.[¶]

[†] *http://wuzzit-trouble.com*
http://www.mathpickle.com
[‡] *http://nrich.maths.org/primary-lower*
http://nrich.maths.org/primary-upper
[§] *http://math.rice.edu/~lanius/frac*
[¶] *http://corbettmaths.com/5-a-day*

Most children enjoy exploring the concept of
infinity with hands-on fractal patterns, such as this
Sierpinski triangle made of tortilla chips.
Fractals are self-similar, which means that subsections of
the object look like smaller versions of the whole thing.

I Thought She Had This

*As we go through each lesson, it seems like my daughter has a good
handle on the concepts, but when we get to the test she forgets everything.
When I ask her about it, she shrugs and says, "I don't know." What do
you do when your child completely loses what she has learned?*

Forgetting is the human brain's natural defense mechanism. It keeps us
from being overwhelmed by the abundance of sensory data that bombards
us each moment of every day. Our children's minds will never work like
a computer that can store a program and recall it flawlessly months later.

Sometimes, for my children, a gentle reminder is enough to drag the
forgotten concept back out of the dust-bunnies of memory. Other times,

I find that they answer "I don't know" out of habit, because it's easier than thinking about the question. And because they'd prefer to be doing something else.

And still other times, I find out they didn't understand the topic as well as I thought they did when we went through it before. No matter how we adults try to explain the concepts, some kids want to be answer-getters. They don't want to do the hard work of thinking a concept through until it makes a connection in their minds. They want to memorize a few steps and crank through the lesson to get it over with.

In all these cases, what helps me the most is conversation. My children and I always talk about our math. I ask questions like "What do you think? What do you remember? Can you explain the question to me? What are they asking for?" And, whether the child's answer is right or wrong, I practice my poker face. Trying not to give anything away, I ask, "How did you figure it out? Can you think of a way to confirm your answer?"

Middle Grade Mishaps

Struggling with Arithmetic

My son can't stand long division or fractions. We had a lesson on geometry, and he enjoyed that—especially the 3-D shapes. If we can just get past the basics, then we'll have time for the things he finds interesting. But one workbook page takes so long, and I'm sick of the drama. Should we keep pushing through?

Those upper-elementary arithmetic topics are important, foundational concepts. Your son needs to master them. But the daily slog through page after page of workbook arithmetic can wear down anyone. Many children find it easier to focus on math when it's built into a game, like those at Colleen King's Math Playground website or on John Golden's Math Hombre Games blog page.[†]

Even if you stick with your textbook, there are ways to make the journey less tedious:

---

† *http://www.mathplayground.com*
http://mathhombre.blogspot.com/p/games.html

- Most children do not need to do every problem on a workbook page, or every page in a section. There is a lot of extra review built into any math program.

- You don't have to finish a section before you work whatever comes after it. Use sticky bookmarks to keep track of your position in two or three chapters at a time, balancing the mundane arithmetic practice with the more interesting topics your son enjoys.

- As much as possible, do math out loud with a whiteboard for scratch work. Somehow, working with colorful markers makes arithmetic more bearable.

- Set a timer for math, and make the time short enough that he feels the end is in sight. I suggest no more than thirty minutes a day for now—and when the timer rings, stop even if you are in the middle of a problem.

Doing math in short sessions has helped us avoid the emotional meltdowns my daughter used to have. Thinking is hard work, and if I ask for too much, she crashes. I prefer to stop before that happens. Because I am sitting with her and working together every problem, I know what she understands and when we can skip a problem (or even jump several lessons), which means that we still get through our book on time.

As healthy as vegetables are, you would never limit your son to eating just lima beans and corn. Similarly, be sure to feed him a varied math diet.

Follow his interest in geometry beyond the standard school topics. Explore tessellations, Escher art, and impossible shapes such as the Penrose triangle. Build Lego scenes—a practical application of 3-D geometry—and maybe even try stop motion animation. Ponder the choices on John Stevens's "Would You Rather?" blog or try some of the challenges at Andrew Stadel's Estimation 180 website. Many of these require three-dimensional reasoning.[†]

---

† *http://wyrmath.com/*
http://www.estimation180.com

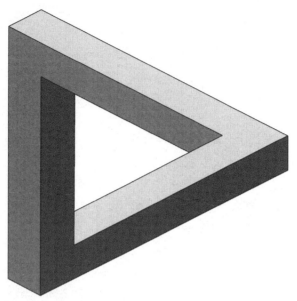

The Penrose triangle is a fun application of 3-D geometry. How is the illusion created? Why can't we build one in the real world?

Suddenly, Nothing Makes Sense

We were doing fine until we hit fractions, but now my son is totally confused. Should we go back and start the book over?

The standard methods for working with fractions require several steps, many of which have sub-steps of their own. Too often, we adults don't appreciate how complex an operation we are asking our children to perform. A fraction calculation is an intricate dance that can seem overwhelming to a beginner.

In most cases, instead of trying to remind your son of all these steps, it's better to help him approach such problems with common sense. His textbook will show the standard method, so your job is to provide some balance, helping your son use whatever math he does remember to think his way through the problems he doesn't (at first) know how to do. For an example of this approach, read my blog post "Subtracting Mixed Numbers: A Cry for Help."[†]

To decide whether to keep going or start over, you first need to find the

---

† *http://denisegaskins.com/2008/03/26/subtracting-mixed-numbers-a-cry-for-help*

source of your son's confusion. When a child who has previously done well hits a wall, it could signal a maturity issue. Math curricula often push children into abstract, formal calculation before they are ready to think that way, so kids learn to survive by rote memorization. Those with analytical minds develop their own ways to understand the rules, but if the math book keeps adding new procedures before the student has made sense of what has come before, the whole process will collapse.

It's natural for parents to assume the trouble is fractions, decimals, long division, algebra, or whatever topic precipitated their child's crash. But the roots of the problem are often hidden in an earlier, foundational topic that your son has not yet mastered.

Math professor Herb Gross explains this with an analogy: "If we gained weight in, say, ten pound increments the chances are that there would be far fewer obese people. The fact is that we usually gain weight a few ounces at a time and that by the time we first notice it, it has been going on for a very long time. The problem is that because we just noticed it, we think that it must have happened recently and therefore it shouldn't take long to remedy the situation. So we diet for an entire weekend, and we are dismayed on Monday morning when we notice that there has been no significant weight loss."

Check your son's long-term mathematical health with one of the assessment websites: Math Reasoning Inventory [if you have trouble with their "sign up for an account" system, don't worry—you don't need an account to use the resources] or Global Strategy Stage Assessment (GloSS). Both of these are one-on-one tests where you read a question, give your son time to think, and then compare what he says to the range of possible responses to determine how well he understands each topic. The Math Reasoning Inventory website includes dozens of videos showing a wide range of student ability, so you can see what sort of answers to expect.[†]

---

† *https://mathreasoninginventory.com/Home/Index*
https://mathreasoninginventory.com/Home/ReasoningOverview
http://www.nzmaths.co.nz/gloss-forms?parent_nod

I've Ruined My Daughter

My daughter is only eleven, but I'm afraid I've ruined her chance of getting into college because she is so far behind in math. We've tried tutors, but she still has trouble, and standardized testing puts her three years below grade level. She was a late reader, too, so maybe school just isn't her thing. What else can I do?

Standardized tests are not placement tests. They cannot tell you at what level your daughter should be studying. They aren't designed that way. The "placement" they give is vague and general, not indicative of her grade level but rather a way of comparing her performance on that particular test with the performance of other students. There can be many different reasons for a low score.

It's possible your daughter has a learning disability or vision or hearing problems that interfere with her schoolwork, since she was a late reader, too. You might want to look into testing for that. Some issues can be fixed with therapy or glasses, while others may require a different approach to math that accommodates the way her brain works.

But if those are not an issue, then don't give up. Middle school is a perfect time to catch up on math. For an encouraging example of how fast a student can progress, read the "Helping a Struggling Math Student" blog post series at Angelicscalliwags. Pay attention to how they started each topic at a simple level to fill in the missing concepts and then increased the difficulty as the girl caught on, so she ended up working problems at her grade level.[†]

My main concern at this point is your daughter's attitude. Does she feel like she's stupid at math? Please take a look at the resources at Jo Boaler's YouCubed site for research-based ways to approach math that can help a discouraged student feel empowered to learn. [‡]

Here's one small change that can make a huge difference: never expect your daughter to do math alone. Brave the daily fight together. Real education, the kind of learning that sticks for a lifetime, comes through relationships. Most children learn more from the give-and-take of simple conversation with an adult than from even the best workbook

---

† *http://angelicscalliwags.com/category/helping-a-struggling-maths-student*
‡ *http://youcubed.org*

or teaching video.

Study together through the archived lessons from Boaler's free Stanford Online course "How to Learn Math: For Students."[†]

Turn math homework into a discussion time. Talk about how she might decide what to try first as she works on a problem or how she could figure out a math fact that slipped from her memory. Talk about your own struggles, where you tend to get confused, and how you persevere, trying different approaches as you muddle through to an answer.

Don't worry too much about grade level. If your daughter is learning and making progress, then she's doing fine. No two children grow at the same rate, physically or academically. There will be some topics that seem easy to her and some that go slower. But take whatever pace fits her learning level, make sure her understanding is firm, and don't worry about being behind an arbitrary number.

High Ability, Low Performance

My son hates math. We are working half a semester behind grade level. He tested low average for math fluency (timed tests) but well above average for reasoning skills. If he was motivated he could do so much, I know! How can I keep him from falling farther behind?

I object to our culture's view that being fluent in math means the ability to ace timed tests. Mathematical fluency ought to mean thinking flexibly about problems and seeing concepts in several ways. After all, we don't call someone fluent in a language because they can pass a timed test, do we? To be fluent in a foreign language means you can understand and converse with a variety of people about almost any topic. Math fluency should mean something like that, too.

Given your son's high score in reasoning skills, I suspect his disinterest in math stems from boredom. Have you considered switching to a curriculum that teaches to his strengths, with an emphasis on logical reasoning and problem solving?

If you are set on your current math program, let him use the chapter review—or whatever they have that is equivalent—as a pretest, and skip the topics he already understands. Don't time this test, since that seems to

---

† *https://www.youcubed.org/category/mooc*

make his brain freeze up. I prefer to do the pretest face to face, with the student explaining the problems he knows how to do. If he gets an answer wrong due to a minor arithmetic glitch, that doesn't matter. But if he can't explain his answer or if he has to skip a problem, those are the lessons we need to study.

Then, when you go through the topics your son missed, consider starting with the hardest problem in each lesson. Ask him what he notices about the problem, which parts seem familiar, which parts seem difficult, and how he might try to figure it out. The challenge of tackling a hard problem is what makes math enjoyable for someone like your son. It's much better to take one worthy problem and find five ways to solve it than to practice one way to solve a routine problem and repeat that five (or ten or fifteen) times.

You may be surprised at how fast he comes up to or even surpasses grade level with an approach like this. Whizzing through a book can do wonders for a student's attitude toward the subject.

The Agonies of Algebra

Losing Track of the Basics

> *My daughter is fairly intuitive with math. We're about half way through our textbook, and her algebra is fine. But basic subtraction? Ugh! She makes a lot of mistakes—always in basic math. How can I make her slow down and pay attention?*

Glitchy mistakes like you describe above are completely normal. Your daughter will never stop making them, no matter how good she is at math. This is why engineers always check each other's work before releasing a project. The mind is not a computer, and when focusing attention on one thing—especially on a new concept, like algebra—it can't spare much attention for everything else, such as those pesky minus signs or the math facts it is so sure it mastered long ago. Result: mental glitch.

My daughter and I do our work together, so when she makes one of these mistakes, I give her "the look," and she knows she needs to double-check it. Often she catches me in similar mistakes. Mental glitches may be more common in teenagers, but none of us are immune.

There are several things that increase my rate of mistakes. You might compare them to your daughter's experience to see if some minor change might make a difference:

- I make more mistakes when I'm tired, fewer when I'm fresh. This is why many homeschoolers try to do math first every day. My daughter and I are not morning people, so that wouldn't help us at all. Instead, we limit our math time to 30–45 minutes a day even in high school, because we've found that her performance (and emotional response) plummets with longer lessons. If we need more time than that, I make sure that we at least take a break.

- I make fewer mistakes when I'm interested in what I'm working on, more when I'm bored or in a hurry. A student who wants to get the lesson over with will tend to make a lot of mistakes.

- I make about the same number of mistakes if I'm working orally, buddy-style, but I tend to catch them faster because of our interaction, so my mental glitch has less chance to ruin the whole answer.

- I make more mistakes when I'm under stress. I don't know your daughter's age, but puberty definitely counts as "under stress" enough to make a mess of mathematical thinking.

- While mental glitches can hit me even on a simple problem, I make more mistakes on complicated, multistep problems. There are so many more chances to make a mistake, and my mind is often rushing ahead to the next step and not paying sufficient attention to the current one.

- I make more mistakes when I'm feeling overwhelmed by something I don't understand, or when I'm trying to remember a lot of rules that haven't become automatic. Think back to when you were learning to drive a car—it's the same feeling.

This last case is a problem that needs attention. A student who is making mistakes for this reason needs help, review, and time to let the new knowledge coalesce. She may need to redo the lesson from a different angle with new explanations that might fit better into her overall understanding. Perhaps she needs to go back to earlier topics to firm up the foundational concepts before coming back to the idea that flummoxed her.

Refuses to Show His Work

No matter how many times I nag my son, he never shows his work. He's studying algebra, but he doesn't seem to have a firm grasp of decimals and fractions. So, more often than not his answers are wrong, but I have no idea what he's doing, and he can't really explain. How can I get him to write out all the steps?

In my opinion, getting stressed out over a teenager not showing his work is like King Canute standing on the shore, commanding the tide not to come in. A classroom teacher has no choice: there will never be enough time to work one-on-one with every student. But a parent or math tutor can make allowances for children who struggle to express their thoughts in writing.

The real problem is that your son is making a lot of mistakes and can't explain what he is doing. The mistakes may be due to plain carelessness, to adolescent forgetfulness, or to deep gaps in his understanding. How can you tell? You could have him work through the Math Reasoning Inventory website I mentioned above or try downloading some targeted worksheets on the subjects that seem his weakest. Or just sit down and go through his algebra lessons together. Work buddy-style, alternating problems down the page. When you work your problems, model the type of explanation you want from him.

And on the chance that adolescence is part of his problem, be prepared for temper tantrums over mistakes and especially over being corrected. I have trouble being patient with such antics, but of course my impatience makes it worse. I went through it myself at that age, didn't you?

Whenever my daughter hits an emotional low, we put the math away. Everything is better when we come back to the same math problem fresh the next day.

Gaps and Standardized Testing

Covering All Our Bases

I grew up homeschooled, and I loved having workbooks and checklists—so of course, my children are exactly the opposite! Part of me is drawn to the idea of learning through playful discovery, of almost unschooling math. But I'm afraid that if I don't have a curriculum, we will miss something important. How can I make sure my kids won't have gaps in their education?

I can guarantee that you will miss something, whether you follow a math curriculum or not. Everyone has gaps in their education—that is the human condition. But if your children learn the basic concepts well, knowing how the math works and why, then they will be able to fill in a gap when they discover it and to learn new material by seeing how it connects to what they already know.

Using a packaged math curriculum will not prevent gaps. But there's another side to the story: using a math program that tries to cover every possible topic might keep your children from gaining a deep understanding of the basics. Your fear of gaps may cause you to make the opposite mistake, providing a "mile wide and inch deep" education.

Don't worry about taking a less formal approach to math in the elementary school years. If you are always doing something—reading library books, telling each other stories, enjoying math crafts, drawing geometric pictures, playing with calendar numbers, and so on—then your children will pick up an amazing amount of knowledge. As Julie Brennan explains: "Early exposure to real mathematics in natural settings, without requiring mastery of arithmetic on a set timetable—this has been a key to the ease with which my kids attain mastery when the time is right for them."

Whichever route you choose, dive into math deeply. Enjoy the adventure of learning. There will be stumbles and struggles along the way. That's how real life is. But if you start with an attitude of playfulness, it will carry you through a lot of the tough times.

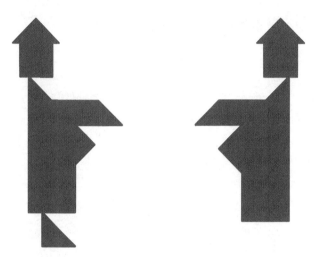

Remember the value of mathematical cross-training.
Puzzles and games teach children to think hard—and enjoy it.
Can your kids explain what happened to the man's
foot in this "Monk in a Mirror" puzzle?
Each figure is made from a single set of tangrams.

How to Recognize Success

After leading co-op math classes for several years, I've become known as the local math maven. Fellow homeschoolers who meet one of my children often say, "Oh, you're Denise's son/daughter? You must be really good at math."

The kids smile politely and try not to roll their eyes until the other person has turned away.

I hear similar comments after presenting a math workshop: "Wow, your kids must love math." But my children are individuals, each with their own interests. They might enjoy an occasional geometry or logic puzzle, but they never voluntarily sit down to slog through a page of exercises.

In fact, one daughter expressed the depth of her youthful perfectionist angst by scribbling all over the cover of her 2nd grade *Miquon Math* workbook: "I hate math! Hate, hate, hate-hate-HATE MATH!!!"

Translation: "If I can't do it flawlessly the first time, then I don't want to do it at all."

I don't judge my success as a math teacher by whether my children enjoy the subject. Neither do I care much about the traditional measures of mathematical success. I don't train my children to recite the math facts. I avoid any sort of timed drill. I'm not interested in how well my children perform in the artificial environment of a standardized test.

How, then, can I tell whether my kids are learning math?

I talk to them.

I ask questions like "How did you figure that out?" or "Why is this true?" and listen hard to their answers. We discuss different ways we could have solved each problem. I watch them as they live their daily lives, keeping my eyes open for clues. Do my children expect math to make sense? Can they explain their reasoning? Do they panic at multistep calculations? Do word problems scare them?

Students who are learning math the mathematician's way will struggle with some topics, as all students do, but they possess an overall expectation that math concepts fit together logically. While they may on occasion get by with memorizing how to solve a certain type of problem, they recognize the danger of relying solely on memory. Their minds will continue to stew over the ideas, either consciously or at a subconscious level, until they get that "Aha!" feeling when the concept connects.

Because they are convinced that math is not arbitrary, these students know that they are capable of figuring things out. When a math problem seems tough, their natural stubbornness kicks in: "No stupid textbook is going to get the best of me." They may stumble, or make careless errors, or forget what they learned last month or even last week. But they know that a generous application of common sense will carry them through almost any mathematical encounter.

Math anxiety is epidemic in our society. Above all else, my goal is to inoculate my children against this disease. Therefore, my number-one yardstick for measuring success is this: *my children do not fear story problems.* Even if they aren't sure how to solve a word problem, my children never look at the math book with a deer-in-the-headlights expression or ask random questions such as "Do I add or multiply?"

After all, they've been playing with math for longer than they can remember. Why should they be afraid?

What About Testing?

As education reformer Jonathan Kozol once said, "If you could lead through testing, the U.S. would lead the world in all education categories. When are people going to understand you don't fatten your lambs by weighing them?"

All that a standardized test can tell you about your child is whether that child is good at taking standardized tests. Each student's test performance depends on:

♦ reading speed, which varies tremendously from one child to the next,

♦ whether the child has the sniffles,

♦ or had an argument with parents the night before,

♦ or finds the questions interesting or not,

♦ or has indigestion,

♦ or forgot to eat breakfast,

♦ or is taking the test in a familiar or unfamiliar setting,

♦ or is worried about a sick pet,

♦ or gives up and answers at random,

♦ or ... well, so many factors!

I'm always grateful if my children do well on the tests, because that can forestall problems with authorities or extended family, and good test scores may help with college admissions. But I've never, ever felt the scores gave me information I didn't already know from working daily with the child.

If you live in a state that requires standardized testing, or if you want to see the test scores to satisfy your own curiosity, please don't let that affect your attitude toward math education. Keep playing around with math the mathematician's way. Let test preparation be a separate area of study. Work through one or more test prep books in the months before a high-stakes standardized test. There are many factors we can't control, but at least we can make sure our children are as familiar as possible with the test format and the types of questions they will see.

But if you want to know how well your children are learning math, don't worry about testing. Instead, ask yourself:

- ◆ Do they understand that common sense applies to math?

- ◆ Can they give logical reasons for their answers?

- ◆ Even when they get confused, do they know that math is nothing to fear?

If so, then be assured: your children are already miles ahead of most of their peers. Their foundations are solid. The details will fall into place as you continue to play with mathematical ideas together.

Congratulations, and keep up the good work.

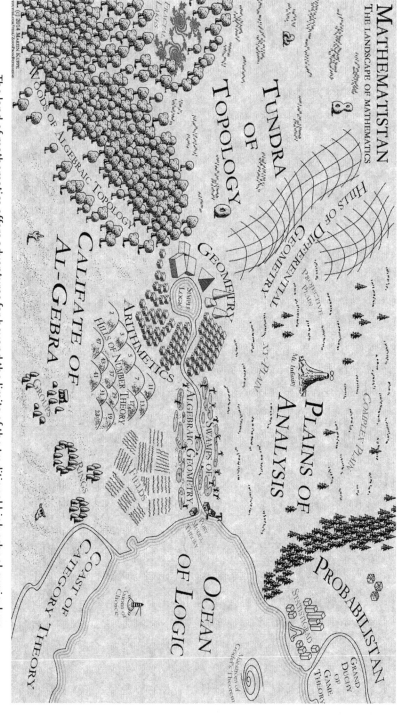

The land of mathematics offers adventures far beyond the limits of the traditional high school curriculum.

184

The high-school English curriculum teaches both the grammar and the poetry. Why can't a high-school mathematics curriculum teach the poetry and artistry of its discipline as well?

—JAMES TANTON

Transition to High School Math

IF YOUR CHILDREN HATE MATH, they probably never got a good taste of the "Aha!" factor, that *Eureka!* thrill of solving a challenging puzzle. The early teen years may be your last chance to convince them that math can be fun, so consider spending a few months on creative math before diving into the abstraction of high school work.

Your family may enjoy:

♦ Subscribing to *Games* magazine.

♦ Reading Brian Bolt books, or working through Raymond Smullyan's *What Is the Name of This Book?*

♦ Designing tessellation T-shirts for Christmas gifts.

♦ Remodeling the house. From financing to floor coverings, that is real math in action.

On the other hand, if you have delayed formal arithmetic, using your children's elementary years to explore a variety of mathematical adventures, now is a good time to take stock of what these experiences have taught your kids. How much of what society considers "the basics" have they picked up along the way? Are there any gaps in their understanding of arithmetic, any concepts you want to add to their mental tool box?

Before you launch into review lessons, watch James Tanton's series of "How to Think like a School Math Genius" videos. He explains five key principles for mathematical thinking that will shape the way you and your teens approach high school math:[†]

- ♦ Visualize: think of a picture.
- ♦ Use common sense to avoid grungy work.
- ♦ Engage in intellectual play.
- ♦ Think relationally: understanding trumps memorization.
- ♦ Be clear on what you don't know—and comfortable enough to admit it.

Tanton gives examples from arithmetic, algebra, and geometry to demonstrate what it means to think about math the mathematician's way, as a game of playing with ideas.

When it comes to math review, many families take advantage of the free videos and computer-graded quizzes at the Khan Academy website. My daughter enjoyed Khan Academy for a couple of weeks, but then the repetitive nature of their randomly-generated problems began to annoy her. I'd rather use Herb Gross's free online Gateways to Mathematics course at AdjectiveNounMath.com. Many of these videos are old-fashioned and slow, but Gross builds on intuition to promote understanding better than many of the flashy new sites I've seen.[‡]

You might also buy a textbook such as *Basic College Mathematics* (choose from several versions by various authors). Old editions are available for pennies—there's no need to pay new-book prices, since arithmetic hasn't changed in centuries. A textbook offers better problems than a computer program can generate, because these problems are carefully selected and arranged to build on each other. You can use the chapter review problems as a pre-test and study only the topics your student needs.

But beware: many books and online resources present mathematics as a follow-the-rules subject. That is fine for review, but if you find a concept that is new to your student, don't be satisfied with just following the

---

[†] *http://www.jamestanton.com/?p=1097*
[‡] *http://www.khanacademy.org*
http://www.adjectivenounmath.com/id74.html

procedure. Memorization can give your kids quick "success," but for most people, memorized rules will not stick in the mind well enough to support future learning. If you find yourself using one of the phrases in Tina Cardone's free ebook *Nix the Tricks: A guide to avoiding shortcuts that cut out math concept development*, that's a warning you need to stop and work on building up conceptual understanding.[†]

If you don't know how to explain a math topic yourself, dig for more information about it. Model the calculation with manipulatives, or draw the shape with drafting tools. Search Kalid Azad's Math Better Explained site for analogies and insights. Where does this topic sit in the mathematical web? Why is it true? How does it relate to other topics?[‡]

You and your student may need to search out several explanations and work your way through dozens of sample problems in order to wrap your minds around a new topic. Wrestling a math concept into submission can be hard. But the work is worth it, because when you are able to help your child truly understand what the math is doing, that concept becomes a rock-solid foundation on which to build.

The Meat of Higher-Level Math

If your children plan to go to college, they will benefit from a serious amount of mathematics in high school. Even those who don't plan on college ought to learn as much as they can because we live in a technological society, and technology runs on math. According to mathematician and author Oleg Gleizer, "Math is freedom. If we don't know math, our choices are so limited."

This does not mean that everyone must follow the traditional algebra-to-calculus sequence. Creative students who want to blaze their own trail of interest-led learning can master the basics of mathematics and then branch out to explore many non-traditional topics, such as logic, discrete math, or game theory.

But first, what are the basics of high school mathematics? What math does everyone need in order to be a math-literate member of our technology-based society?

---

† *http://nixthetricks.com*
‡ *http://betterexplained.com*

Everyone Needs Algebra

Many people think that algebra is "the rules and procedures for doing math with letters," and they can't imagine ever using it in real life. But algebra is much deeper, richer, and more important than just rules and procedures.

Algebra is:

♦ Using the things you know to figure out something you don't know.

♦ Thinking about the relationships between things, how changing one thing affects everything else.

Things we know, things we don't know, and the relationships between them—such is the stuff of real life. Algebra gives us the tools to model, understand, and solve the problems we face at home and at work, from shipping to science, politics to planning retirement.

Everyone Needs Geometry

Geometry is not just formulas, two-column proofs, and memorizing definitions to pass a test. Like algebra, geometry is deeper, richer, and more important than most people realize.

Geometry is:

♦ Using the shapes and properties we know to figure out something we don't know.

♦ Thinking about the relationships between things, how changing one thing affects everything else.

We live in a three-dimensional world, surrounded by length and height and breadth. From crafts to construction, marketing to medicine, property development to playing in virtual worlds—shapes, volumes, and the relationships between them affect almost everything we do.

Everyone Needs Statistics

No one can be considered an educated adult in our society without a basic understanding of statistics—of what the numbers mean and especially of what they do not mean. The modern world is an ocean of data. Waves of information buffet us from every direction. Our students need to learn how to obtain, analyze, synthesize, evaluate, and draw inferences from statistics.

Online Resources for High School Math

The free resources in this section will appeal to unschoolers and independent learners who want to dabble in the different areas of high school math before committing themselves to deeper study. This is only a sample of the gems waiting to be discovered online. You can find more in the appendix or on my blog's resource pages, and new websites are being created every day.[†]

Families who follow a more traditional approach may also find these links useful. There will be times when the standard curriculum is not enough. Your children may read their textbook or watch a video lesson several times and work through every sample problem, yet still have trouble understanding a concept. In cases like that, it helps to look up a different explanation that can give your child a new way of looking at the topic.

Whichever category describes your family, keep in mind what Albert Einstein said: "Learning is experience. Everything else is just information."

In math, *experience* means grappling with and solving problems. Even the most useful website can only provide information. If we want our teenage students to learn mathematics, they will have to build their own experience by working their way through lots and lots of math problems.

Where can you find good problems to learn on? Phillips Exeter Academy has posted an entire high school curriculum made up only of problems.[‡] If you like James Tanton's common-sense approach to math, consider his high school curriculum series *Thinking Mathematics*.[§] Or for a more liberal-arts approach, try a free textbook from the Discovering the

---

[†]   *http://denisegaskins.com/internet-math-resources*
[‡]   *http://www.exeter.edu/academics/72_6539.aspx*
[§]   *http://www.jamestanton.com/?page_id=20*

Art of Mathematics website.[†]

Algebra

Please don't let your children flounder in algebra: the Internet is overflowing with help. For instance, many kids need hands-on exploration to help them wrap their brains around a new math concept. Henri Picciotto offers a selection of interesting activities at A New Algebra.[‡]

You can stretch your students' mathematical modeling skills with Fawn Nguyen's Visual Patterns blog. Pick any design you like and practice recognizing, describing, and predicting the pattern. Or help your kids develop an intuitive understanding of functions and graphs with the videos at Dan Meyer's Graphing Stories.[§]

Does your child need a refresher lesson on negative numbers or the exponent rules? For quick explanations of prealgebra and algebra topics, try visiting Elizabeth Stapel's Purplemath site. Or check out James Tanton's video lessons for "true and joyous" ways to understand a variety of high school math topics. Your student may also enjoy Tanton's free online courses at G'Day Math.[¶]

John Golden suggests several websites that offer algebra and geometry lessons in his blog post, "Such a Thing as Free." You might also take a look at Herb Gross's Algebra by Example (step-by-step, problem-based learning), Murray Bourne's Interactive Mathematics (a wide-ranging site full of interesting stuff), and the West Texas A&M Virtual Math Lab (preparation for college-level math). One of these is bound to fit your family's learning style.[**]

Art of Problem Solving offers a terrific supplement to any algebra program with their video lessons featuring Richard Rusczyk, who is always entertaining. And be sure to take advantage of their online learn-

---

[†] *https://www.artofmathematics.org/books*
[‡] *http://www.mathedpage.org/new-algebra/new-algebra.html*
[§] *http://www.visualpatterns.org*
http://www.graphingstories.com
[¶] *http://www.purplemath.com/modules/index.htm*
http://www.jamestanton.com/?cat=6
http://gdaymath.com/courses
[**] *http://mathhombre.blogspot.com/2014/10/such-thing-as-free.html*
http://www.adjectivenounmath.com/id79.html
http://www.intmath.com/basic-algebra/basic-algebra-intro.php
http://www.wtamu.edu/academic/anns/mps/math/mathlab

ing system, Alcumus, where students can practice their problem-solving skills.[†]

Geometry

The best way to learn geometry is to play with geometric objects such as lines, curves, angles and shapes. The Maths Is Fun site offers a quick overview of geometry topics, including vocabulary and how to draw various shapes. Or explore the free math software GeoGebra, with its wealth of user-created instructional materials for all ages.[‡]

My favorite part of geometry was learning to do constructions, drawing shapes and designs with a compass and straightedge. Nico Disseldorp's Let's Play: Ancient Greek Geometry website makes a game of completing various construction puzzles in a certain number of moves. The screen starts out with two dots. If you click and drag from one point to the other, it makes a line segment. Dragging in any other direction will make a circle. If you stop when your circle intersects the second point, you'll create a circle with the original distance as radius. Now try drawing two circles: their intersections will offer new points to work from.[§]

[†] *http://artofproblemsolving.com/videos*
http://www.artofproblemsolving.com/alcumus
[‡] *http://www.mathsisfun.com/geometry/index.html*
http://www.geogebra.org/cms
[§] *http://sciencevsmagic.net/geo*

For more than two millennia, people have struggled with and mastered Euclidean geometry as the foundation for higher math and logic. It's still a great way for students to sharpen their thinking skills, as long as they approach each theorem as a puzzle to understand rather than as a rule to memorize. In 1847, Oliver Byrne published an innovative, pictorial version called *The first six books of the Elements of Euclid, in which coloured diagrams and symbols are used instead of letters.*[†]

Lawrence Spector explains Euclid's Book I, with interactive quizzes along the way. Or check out David E. Joyce's Interactive Euclid's Elements, which includes all thirteen books, with Java applets to demonstrate each theorem.[‡]

The great advances of modern math and science began when geometry and algebra learned to dance together on a coordinate grid. Your students can explore the relationships between equations and shapes with the Desmos Graphing Calculator and try their hands at some of the Daily Desmos blog challenges.[§]

Statistics

Many students have enjoyed the classic *How to Lie with Statistics* by Darrell Huff: "The crooks already know these tricks; honest men must learn them in self-defense." The book is older than I am (in the first chapter, $25,000/year is considered a salary that a Yale graduate might boast about), but it is still in print, and the information is as relevant as your daily newspaper. Maybe more so, since newspapers routinely commit many of the errors Huff warns against.[¶]

For a more modern take on the difficulties of interpreting numbers, read Gary Smith's *Standard Deviations: Flawed Assumptions, Tortured Data, and Other Ways to Lie with Statistics.*

Robert Niles wrote his online "Statistics Every Writer Should Know" tutorial for math-phobic journalists or anyone else who wants to master the basics.[**]

[†] *https://www.math.ubc.ca/~cass/Euclid/byrne.html*
https://archive.org/details/firstsixbooksofe00eucl
[‡] *http://www.themathpage.com/aBookI/plane-geometry.htm*
http://aleph0.clarku.edu/~djoyce/java/elements/elements.html
[§] *https://www.desmos.com*
http://dailydesmos.com
[¶] *https://archive.org/details/HowToLieWithStatistics*
[**] *http://www.robertniles.com/stats*

Modern statistical questions often deal with *conditional probabilities.* They ask, "If statement A is true, then what are the chances that statement B is also true?" For instance, we know that medical tests aren't perfect. If the test came back positive, what are the chances that I have the disease? To answer questions like this, you need Bayesian statistics. For a quick introduction, read the *New York Times* article "The Odds, Continually Updated," or Kevin Boone's Bayesian Statistics for Dummies webpage.[†]

One of the most important lessons for any statistics student is, "Correlation does not imply causation." For example, department stores stock their shelves with shorts, flip-flops, and swimsuits. Soon afterward, ice cream sales begin to climb. Did skimpy clothes cause people to crave frozen desserts? Tyler Vigen takes statistical humor to new heights at his blog, Spurious Correlations.[‡]

Your students may also enjoy browsing Michael Friendly's Gallery of Data Visualization, which features several of the world's best (and worst) statistical graphs. As the author points out, seeing may or may not lead to believing, but "above all, data analysis involves visual, as well as statistical, understanding."[§]

When your students are ready to dig deeper into formal statistics, check out Stan Brown's Stats Without Tears course book and related materials. Or try Rice University's online Statistics Education: A Multimedia Course of Study or Carnegie Mellon's open learning course in probability and statistics.[¶]

Are You Ready for a Textbook?

A mathematics textbook can be a wonderful learning tool for students who know how to use it. A good textbook offers clear explanations of mathematical concepts and an assortment of worked-out sample problems to demonstrate procedures. It can help students become fluent in the

---

[†]   *http://www.nytimes.com/2014/09/30/science/the-odds-continually-updated.html*
http://www.kevinboone.net/bayes.html
[‡]   *http://www.tylervigen.com*
[§]   *http://www.datavis.ca/gallery/index.php*
[¶]   *http://brownmath.com/swt*
http://onlinestatbook.com/2/index.html
http://oli.cmu.edu/courses/free-open/statistics-course-details

language of math and learn how to represent their thoughts so that others can understand them.

Most important, a math textbook provides a rich source of practice problems, arranged in order of increasing difficulty, which offer students the chance to gain the kind of experience that builds true mathematical learning.

Unfortunately, too many students make the mistake of reading a lesson straight through as if it were a story, and too few of them attempt each sample problem before reading the book's solution. To get off on the right foot, encourage your children to read Stan Brown's detailed instructions about "How to Read a Math Book" and "How to Study Math."[†]

Don't be fooled by your own history of dry or tedious math classes: textbook mathematics is still math the mathematician's way, as mental play. But it is no longer the play of a child dabbling in the shallows, nor the play of the couch potato who wants only to observe. No, this is the play of the athlete, who works hard at training and enjoys seeing his muscles grow firm, who can't wait to test himself against a challenging opponent. As the athlete does not simply memorize rules and procedures, but instead analyzes the game until it makes sense and practices every move, no matter how difficult, until it feels natural—so the student must work with each math concept until it becomes a part of himself.

"Study actively," mathematician Paul Halmos urges. "Don't just read it; fight it! Ask your own questions, look for your own examples, discover your own proofs."

Anything else, as Einstein said, is merely information.

Choosing a Math Program

When I started homeschooling, the only choices for high school math were textbooks written for classrooms. Now, there are an almost frightening number of choices. All the old options are still around, but they've been joined by math programs written for home schools, video programs taught by college professors, and interactive online courses. How are we to choose?

To make matters more difficult, we must recognize that no textbook

---

† *http://brownmath.com/stfa*

or math program is perfect. Each family is different. Even within a family, what works for one child may fail miserably with another. After more than a quarter-century of experience, I'm still reduced to guessing which program will interest my youngest daughter and then adjusting my expectations as we work our way through the book.

Any book can show your teen how to substitute numbers into an equation. If you want them to learn the art of solving problems, however, you will have to choose your book with care. Use the following questions to help you compare the materials you find at curriculum fairs or book sales:

♦ Does the author tell you why a topic is important? Does the book relate mathematical ideas to each other and to real life, or is math something you learn just because it will be on the test?

♦ Does the book help students learn to think? Does it explain the reasoning behind the rules, or does it emphasize procedures? Is the student expected to reason things out, or to follow instructions and fill in the blanks?

♦ Do the homework problems seem interesting, or are they busywork? Does the book provide at least a few deep and playful problems? Can students taste the "Aha!" factor?

♦ As a pianist needs scales and football players need training camp, so high school math students need plenty of practice mastering

Fencing with tangrams. Athletes work hard to build skills and endurance. In the same way, math students who want to move beyond the basics must work with determination and perseverance.

each new skill. Are there enough homework problems that they can internalize the rules of the game? Does the book provide opportunities for reviewing prior topics?

♦ Is the book at all attractive? A math book doesn't need glossy photos or magazine-style sidebars, but read a few of the lessons and ask yourself, "Would I want to spend 150 hours with the author?"

Which math program you choose will depend on how comfortable you are with math yourself and what you want for your children. If you feel totally out of your depth in high school math, you may want to try a video series or hire a local tutor. Either of these choices can be expensive, but students will learn much more with a mentor who knows and enjoys the subject. To parents who suffer from math anxiety, that may be well worth the money.

Working Yourself Out of a Job

If your children have a strong foundation of understanding elementary and middle-school math, and if they are mature enough to recognize when they need to ask for help, they might be able to do their high school math independently. You may find yourself serving more as occasional consultant than as daily instructor. Even if you never studied trigonometry, a few Socratic questions will often lead your student toward the answer.

Review the problem-solving questions in Chapter 5 (page 100) as a guide for what to ask:

♦ Describe your problem to me.

♦ What do you know? What information do they give you?

♦ What do you want? What are you trying to find?

♦ What do you know that is *not* stated in the problem?

♦ How are the pieces of the problem related to each other?

♦ Can you represent the information with a diagram, graph, chart, or table? Would that help you see a pattern?

♦ What can you do? Tell me what you've already tried.

- Have you had a problem similar to this one before?

- Which steps do you feel confident about?

- What might you change?

- Can you tell me a method that would *not* work on this problem? Why not?

- What makes this problem different from the others?

- What is the hardest or most frustrating part of this problem? How would you figure the rest of it out, if that part wasn't there?

- Can you think of any way to eliminate that hardest part?

- Can you think of a way to test your solution?

- Will your strategy work in other problems?

When I first studied calculus, my dad helped me through at least one killer problem in every homework set this way, just by asking questions. He later admitted to me that even though he was a professional engineer, he hadn't known exactly what I was supposed to be doing—but I never would have guessed that. His questions were enough to spark my memory of something we had done in class or of an earlier problem that helped me work through the place where I was stumped.

When You Get Stuck

It happens to everyone: your students hit a challenging problem in a new topic. No matter what they try, nothing seems to work. You watch the video together or read the textbook again, but it doesn't make any sense. How can you help when math traps your kids in its jaws and threatens to chew them up? Wouldn't it be great if you could call up someone who knows what to do?

When you need someone to explain a mysterious math concept, many public libraries or tax-supported community colleges offer free homework help to members of the community. Or thanks to the Internet, you can chat with math people at almost any time of day or night through an online discussion forum.

Math teacher Elizabeth Stapel offers advice for elementary through high school students and their parents at her Purplemath Forums.[†]

The Living Math Forum is a community of parents and teachers devoted to non-traditional math methods and resources for helping children learn math. Don't ask about specific homework problems, but it's a great place to find help with conceptual questions.[‡]

The Free Math Help Forum offers help and advice on topics from arithmetic to differential equations. The Math Help Forum offers help for algebra and beyond.[§]

S.O.S. CyberBoard is a topical help forum for high school and college-level mathematics, engineering, computer science, and more.[¶]

The Art of Problem Solving forum offers help for middle school and older students, focusing on the puzzling challenge problems found in math competitions.[**]

Extra Credit Adventures

Once students have a solid foundation in algebra and geometry, and a decent introductory understanding of statistics, everything else in high school math is "extra credit." This means your students can study whatever they like. Try not to limit your family to the topics in a math textbook, but give your kids freedom to range over the whole domain of mathematics. Play with ideas, numbers, shapes, and patterns. Ask questions. What do you notice? What do you wonder?

Your students won't be able to understand everything they find, but they will discover interesting things that they can understand—and as their knowledge grows, so will their confidence.

For example ...

Thinking Skills

Sometime in middle school or high school, you may want to work together with your child through the book *Thinking Mathematically* by John Mason

---

† *http://www.purplemath.com/learning/index.php*
‡ *https://groups.yahoo.com/neo/groups/LivingMathForum/info*
§ *http://www.freemathhelp.com/forum/forum.php*
http://mathhelpforum.com/math-help-forum.php
¶ *http://www.sosmath.com/CBB/index.php*
** *http://www.artofproblemsolving.com/community*

et al. Get a spiral notebook or journal for each person. Go through the book at your own pace. Take time to think about the problems, even just one problem per week. This is serious practice in mathematical reasoning, how to tackle a tough question or problem in a creatively logical way. As the authors write: "A great deal more can be learned from an unsuccessful attempt than from a question which is quickly resolved, provided you think about it earnestly, make use of techniques suggested in the book, and reflect on what you have done. Answers are irrelevant to the main purpose of this book. The important thing is to experience the processes being discussed."

For online adventures in thinking hard, take a look at Stella's Stunners or the problem sets from the Julia Robinson Math Festival.[†]

Or check your library for Bonnie Averbach and Orin Chein's *Problem Solving Through Recreational Mathematics*, Paul Lockhart's *Measurement*, or Paul Zeitz's *The Art and Craft of Problem Solving*.

Ready for a more abstract challenge? Try your hand at college-level math with Keith Devlin's online Introduction to Mathematical Thinking course or Ted Sundstrom's *Mathematical Reasoning: Writing and Proof.*[‡]

Programming

Writing code for a computer to read requires logical thinking and precise attention to detail. If your child, like mine, dreams of a career as a game programmer, here are a few places to start:

Scratch is a programming language developed at MIT that makes it easy for students to create interactive stories, animations, games, music, and art—and share those creations on the web. Or explore the downloadable Alice system that allows students to learn coding concepts as they create animated movies and simple video games.[§]

Code.org offers game-like tutorials for beginners and beyond. Codecademy offers interactive lessons in a variety of programming languages,

---

[†] *http://www.ohiorc.org/for/math/stella*
http://jrmf.org/problems.php
[‡] *https://www.coursera.org/course/maththink*
http://scholarworks.gvsu.edu/books/9
[§] *http://scratch.mit.edu*
http://www.alice.org/index.php

along with project ideas and forums for asking questions.[†]

My daughter has enjoyed working through Al Sweigart's free *Invent Your Own Computer Games with Python* books. Each chapter gives your student the complete source code for a new game and then teaches programming concepts from the example.[‡]

Green Tea Press offers a couple of free programming books for high school or college students: *How to Think like a Computer Scientist* and *Think Python*.[§]

Computer programmers need to understand and use discrete math, which includes permutations, probability, number theory, and more—fun topics that are often left out of the standard progression of school mathematics. A good place to start is James Tanton's short Permutations and Combinations video course. Art of Problem Solving offers a series of Counting & Probability videos, and their Alcumus interactive learning system includes counting, probability, and number theory puzzles.[¶]

Advanced students will want to test their skills with the Project Euler challenge. The problems vary in difficulty, and you do not have to take them in order. How far through the list can your student go?[**]

Trigonometry

Trigonometry begins with the relationships between the sides and angles of a right triangle, but it ends up affecting almost everything in the world. Anyone headed for college math, science, or engineering needs to master trig. David Eisenberg's Discovering Trigonometry with Sticks and Shadows is a great place to start.[††]

And be sure to explore trig functions and polar coordinate graphing on the Desmos Calculator.[‡‡]

Trigonometric identities are monster algebra puzzles that relate one

---

[†] *http://code.org/learn*
http://www.codecademy.com
[‡] *http://inventwithpython.com*
[§] *http://greenteapress.com/thinkcpp/index.html*
http://greenteapress.com/thinkpython/thinkpython.html
[¶] *http://gdaymath.com/courses/permutations-and-combinations*
http://www.artofproblemsolving.com/videos
http://artofproblemsolving.com/alcumus
[**] *http://projecteuler.net*
[††] *http://www.catcode.com/trig*
[‡‡] *https://www.desmos.com*

trig function to another. Students often attempt to rote-memorize these, but there are far too many of them, and they all begin to look alike. Instead, read Stan Brown's Trig Without Tears website to discover the few identities you need to learn and how to reason out all the rest from those.[†]

Calculus

Like brainteasers and logic puzzles, calculus is mind-bender math: finite mankind attempting to grasp infinity. For most students, calculus hits like a tsunami of abstract nonsense. If your students are ready to try the big one, call up the mathematical Coast Guard: *Calculus Made Easy,* by Silvanus P. Thompson.[‡]

Thompson explains: "Considering how many fools can calculate [that is, use calculus], it is surprising that it should be thought either a difficult or a tedious task for any other fool to learn how to master the same tricks. What one fool can do, another can!"

Calculus may not be "easy," despite Thompson's optimistic title, but it shouldn't be quite as hard as most people expect it to be, assuming your student has a strong mathematical background. But be aware that calculus ramps up the level of work in the same way that middle-school math (percents, decimals, ratios, etc.) ramped up the difficulty level compared to primary school. If there is any weakness in your student's foundational understanding of algebra or trigonometry, calculus will find it.

You can review the most important concepts of precalculus math at the Cool Math website. Or work through the trigonometry and precalculus topics at The Math Page.[§]

Enjoy a friendly introduction to calculus topics with *Prof. E. McSquared's Calculus Primer* by Howard Swann and John Johnson. Or dig deeper with *The Manga Guide to Calculus* by Hiroyuki Kojima and Shin Togami.

Check out Karl's Calculus for handy tutorials and sample problems. Karl Hahn has a creative way of explaining the ideas, and I enjoyed reading his lessons. Kalid Azad takes an intuitive, often visual, approach to

---

† *http://brownmath.com/twt*
‡ *http://djm.cc/library/Calculus_Made_Easy_Thompson.pdf (PDF)*
§ *http://www.coolmath.com/precalculus-review-calculus-intro*
http://www.themathpage.com/aTrig/trigonometry.htm
http://www.themathpage.com/aPreCalc/precalculus.htm

understanding in Calculus Better Explained.[†]

Ready for a calculus textbook? Download the *Active Calculus* book and follow the accompanying videos. Or explore the inquiry-based Calculus Concepts and Applications course.[‡]

And More

For extra-curricular mathematical adventures, encourage students to investigate the mathematical miscellany at Alexander Bogomolny's Cut the Knot website, explore famous problems in the history of mathematics, or research the history of mathematical games and recreations.[§]

Your whole family could get lost wandering through the archives of the Math Munch blog, a weekly digest of delicious math activities, projects, artwork, and games on the Internet.[¶]

Martin Gardner's math articles from the *Scientific American* magazine inspired a generation of budding mathematicians and scientists. Now collected in book form, they are as fascinating as ever. Look up the 793.74 puzzle book shelves at your public library, or start with *The Colossal Book of Mathematics: Classic Puzzles, Paradoxes, and Problems*.

A student who enjoys science fiction may want to explore *Relativity in Illustrations* by Jacob Schwartz, *Flatland* by Edwin Abbott, or *Geometry, Relativity and the Fourth Dimension* by Rudolf Rucker. None of these books are easy reading, but neither are they out of reach of a determined teenager.[**]

Almost everyone likes the amazing hyperbolic art of M. C. Escher. To learn the math behind those drawings, visit Joel Castellanos's Non-Euclid website where your students can play around with the mind-blowingly weird world of hyperbolic geometry for themselves.[††]

---

† *http://web.archive.org/web/20140517212513/http://karlscalculus.org*
http://betterexplained.com/calculus
‡ *http://scholarworks.gvsu.edu/books/10*
https://opencalculus.wordpress.com/2015/08/25/screencasts-for-active-calculus
http://www.iblcalculus.com/home
§ *http://www.cut-the-knot.org*
http://mathforum.org/isaac/mathhist.html
http://www-groups.dcs.st-and.ac.uk/~history/HistTopics/Mathematical_games.html
¶ *http://mathmunch.org*
** *http://www.ibiblio.org/eldritch/eaa/FL.HTM*
†† *http://www.josleys.com/show_gallery.php?galid=325*
http://cs.unm.edu/~joel/NonEuclid/NonEuclid.html

Even in high school, if you get your kids hooked on the challenge of mathematics as mental play, they will never be satisfied with mere textbook math. There is always something fascinating just around the corner.

Children learning math by adding up the costs of a
shopping list in a classroom grocery shop at Fen Ditton
Junior School, Cambridgeshire in December 1944.

Many who have never had the occasion to discover more about mathematics consider it a dry and arid science. In reality, however, it is a science that demands the greatest imagination.

—Sofia Kovalevskaya

Conclusion: Growing Up with Math

FROM THE TIME WE BEGIN counting with our toddlers to the day our students graduate, our goal never changes. At every age and stage of development, we want our children to see math the mathematician's way: as a mental game, playing with ideas. Therefore, we adults train ourselves to model such play, to show interest in our child's ideas, and to ask questions: "What do you see? What do you think? How can we know? How did you figure it out?"

A Gentle Start: Do No Harm

We want children to see math as interesting and inviting, not threatening. This does not mean we avoid difficult topics—that would just be boring. But we treat our youngsters as human persons, not as little calculators we can program, nor as pets we can train to do math tricks. We encourage them to use their natural intuition to reason about numbers, rather than expecting them to memorize formal rules and procedures.

Human beings are social animals, so our math is social, too. We play with, count, and compare sets of toys or candies, and we try to imagine what it would be like to collect infinity. We talk about the natural, fractal-like shapes and symmetries we see as we walk through the park and contrast these with the simpler, man-made patterns at the mall. We ask our child to make up problems for us to solve, and even as we say, "Oooh, that's a tough one," we are glad for the chance to model problem solving.

Young children thrive on stories and imaginative play, but they struggle with the abstractness of written math. For most kids in this stage, written work ought to be a small part of their math experience. So we do as much as we can orally and encourage our children to use manipulatives as long as they find them helpful.

If we plan math lessons, these are short and as game-like as possible. For instance, we might play the doubling game together: you pick a number, and I'll double it. Then you double that, and then it is my turn again. How high can we go before our mental math skills give out?

As They Mature: Applied Common Sense

As children grow in their ability to imagine and reason about abstract concepts, our mathematical discussions become more abstract. Yet we are careful not to work against our children's intuitive understanding by forcing them to follow our rules. Instead, we expect them to think about why a math rule works, compare it to their natural reasoning, and then choose the problem-solving method they prefer.

We recognize that children are short-term thinkers, wanting to finish their school work with as little effort as possible so they can get back to the truly important things in life, such as Minecraft. We resist their efforts to turn math into answer-getting and insist on their taking time to explain and justify their conclusions.

Most older students prefer to draw pictures or use their imagination rather than work with manipulatives, but we keep the physical math tools handy to use as needed. Written work becomes more important over the years, but we are careful not to let our workbook become a slave-master. We are especially wary of assigning pages of independent, repetitive practice—while we know that repetition is essential to build math skills, we prefer to develop these skills in the context of a game or puzzle.

Math lessons are often longer and more formal now, but we remember that thinking hard can be just as tiring as physical labor. We watch for signs of emotional fatigue. We may even split our scheduled math time into two parts: a short session of working together for conceptual work, learning new topics, and a separate time for more playful work such as online math games.

In Everything, Seek Understanding

We are never satisfied with only knowing how to solve a math problem, but always try to find out why the math works the way it does. Is it connected to other topics we have studied? What are the similarities? What are the differences? What happens to the outcome if we change something? How does this relate to foundational concepts such as place value, symmetry, pattern-making, or growth?

As math becomes more advanced, we may be forced to approach new concepts as an abstract game for which we must learn procedures that seem arbitrary. But as we master the rules of the game, we relish the challenge of learning to play the game well. We take pains to search out the ideas and relationships that underlie those rules, so we can understand how to apply them to new problems.

In the few years we have our children at home, we cannot possibly teach them everything they will need to know as adults. At best, we can give them the tools for learning and the ability to reason, so they can continue their own education. And one of the most important tools for learning is a solid understanding of real mathematics—math taught the mathematician's way, as mental play.

I've spent the last two days going over my problem,
going over my approach,
finding new gaps in my proof,
fixing them … wash, rinse, repeat.

It's amazing that this vision of math
as "getting to the right answer
on your first try"
even exists.
I have to make, unmake, remake
so many mistakes
to get where I'm going.

I think all mathematicians work that way.
Math doesn't happen in a straight line.
If I hadn't made as many mistakes
in my thinking about this problem,
I don't think I would have solved it.

Somehow, a big part of the experience of math is trouble.
Frustration is the status quo.
But when you get something—the thrill!

—DAN FINKEL

Resources and References

"Living" Math Books for All Ages

Most of these books should be available through your local library or via interlibrary loan. Check for instruction books in the 510–519 range in the Dewey decimal system, and look for logic puzzles at 793.74. Many of the old books have fallen out of print, but they are still excellent. For even more books (with links), check out my Math with Living Books blog pages.

http://denisegaskins.com/living-math-books

And if you find a great book I have missed, please write and tell me. I will put it on my interlibrary loan list right away.

For Parents and Teachers

Adding It Up: Helping Children Learn Mathematics by Jeremy Kilpatrick, et al.

Children Doing Mathematics by Terezinha Nunes and Peter Bryant

Children's Mathematics: Cognitively Guided Instruction by Thomas P. Carpenter, et al.

Creative Problem Solving in School Mathematics by George Lenchner

Dr. Wright's Kitchen Table Math by Chris Wright

Elementary Mathematics for Teachers and *Elementary Geometry for Teachers* by Thomas H. Parker and Scott J. Baldridge

Extending Children's Mathematics: Fractions & Decimals by Susan B. Empson and Linda Levi

Family Math by Stenmark, et al.

First Grade Diary by Lore Rasmussen

Games for Math by Peggy Kaye

Good Questions for Math Teaching: Why Ask Them and What to Ask, Grades K–6 by Peter Sullivan and Pat Lilburn, *Grades 5–8* by Nancy Canavan Anderson and Lainie Schuster

How to Homeschool Math—Even If You Hate Fractions!! by Robin Padron

How to Solve It: A New Aspect of Mathematical Method by George Polya

Knowing and Teaching Elementary Mathematics: Teachers' Understanding of Fundamental Mathematics in China and the United States by Liping Ma

Math by Kids! A Collection of Word Problems Written by Kids for Kids of All Ages edited by Susan Richman

Math from Three to Seven: The Story of a Mathematical Circle for Preschoolers by Alexander Zvonkin, *Mathematical Circle Diaries, Year 1: Complete Curriculum for Grades 5 to 7* by Anna Burago, and other books in the MSRI Mathematical Circles Library series

Math You Can Play series by Denise Gaskins

Mathematical Activities: A Resource Book for Teachers and other books by Brian Bolt

A Mathematician's Lament: How School Cheats Us out of Our Most Fascinating and Imaginative Art Form by Paul Lockhart

Mindset: The New Psychology of Success by Carol Dweck

Moebius Noodles: Adventurous Math for the Playground Crowd by Yelena McManaman and Maria Droujkova

The Myth of Ability: Nurturing Mathematical Talent in Every Child by John Mighton

Nix the Tricks: A guide to avoiding shortcuts that cut out math concept development by Tina Cardone

Number Sense Routines: Building Numerical Literacy Every Day in Grades K–3 by Jessica F. Shumway

Number Talks: Helping Children Build Mental Math and Computation Strategies, Grades K–5 by Sherry Parrish

Old Dogs, New Math: Homework Help for Puzzled Parents by Mike Askew and Rob Eastaway

Playing with Math: Stories from Math Circles, Homeschoolers, and Passionate Teachers edited by Sue VanHattum

Talking Math with Your Kids and other books by Christopher Danielson

The Teaching Gap: Best Ideas from the World's Teachers for Improving Education in the Classroom by James W. Stigler, James Hiebert

Teaching Student-Centered Mathematics: Developmentally Appropriate Instruction by John A. Van de Walle et al.

Vision in Elementary Mathematics and other books by W. W. Sawyer

What's Math Got to Do with It? How Teachers and Parents Can Transform Mathematics Learning and Inspire Success by Jo Boaler

Preschool to Early Elementary

Anything by Greg Tang, Tana Hoban, or Mitsumasa Anno

12 Ways to Get to 11 by Eve Merriam

A Fly on the Ceiling by Julie Glass

Apple Fractions by Jerry Pallotta

Ben Franklin and the Magic Squares by Frank Murphy

Blockhead: The Life of Fibonacci by Joseph D'Agnese

The Boy Who Loved Math: The Improbable Life of Paul Erdos by Deborah Heiligman

Camp Logic by Mark Saul and Sian Zelbo

Count On Your Fingers African Style by Claudia Zaslavsky

Dear Benjamin Banneker by Andrea Davis Pinkne

Each Orange Had 8 Slices by Paul Giganti

Fraction Fun by David A. Adler

Full House by Dayle Ann Dodds

Grandfather Tang's Story by Ann Tompert

Growing Patterns by Sarah C. Campbell

How Much Is a Million? and other books by David Schwartz

The Librarian Who Measured the Earth by Kathryn Lasky

MathStart series by Stuart J. Murphy

Multiplying Menace and *The Multiplying Menace Divides* by Pam Calvert

Of Numbers and Stars: The Story of Hypatia by D. Anne Love

One Hundred Hungry Ants and *A Remainder of One* by Elinor J. Pinczes

Rabbits, Rabbits Everywhere: A Fibonacci Tale by Ann McCallum

Sir Cumference series by Cindy Neuschwander

Spaghetti and Meatballs for All! and *The Greedy Triangle* by Marilyn Burns

Tangramables by Judi Martschinke

Ten, Nine, Eight by Molly Bang

Three Pigs, One Wolf, Seven Magic Shapes by Grace Maccarone

The Time-Life *I Love Math* series (various authors)

What's Your Angle, Pythagoras? A Math Adventure by Julie Ellis

Which One Doesn't Belong? by Christopher Danielson (2016)

You Can Count on Monsters by Richard Evan Schwartz

Young Math Books series by Crowell (various authors)

Upper-Elementary and Middle School

Many of the above, plus:

The Adventures of Penrose the Mathematical Cat and other books by Theoni Pappas

The Amazing Mathematical Amusement Arcade and other books by Brian Bolt

Archimedes and the Door of Science by Jeanne Bendick

Can You Count in Greek?: Exploring Ancient Number Systems by Judy Leimbach

Carry On, Mr. Bowditch by Jean Lee Latham

The Cat in Numberland by Ivar Ekeland

Challenge Math and other books by Ed Zaccaro

Classic Brain Teasers by Martin Gardner

Compass Drawings by Linda Nelson Harst and Margaret Sayre Wiederhold

Competition Math for Middle School by J. Batterson

Cool Math! by Christy Maganzini

Curve Stitching: Art of Sewing Beautiful Mathematical Patterns by Jon Millington

Do You Wanna Bet? by Jean Cushman

Fibonacci Fun by Trudi Hammel Garland

G is for Googol by David Schwarz

Geometrical Design, Visual Illusions and other coloring books from Dover

Go Figure! A Totally Cool Book about Numbers by Johnny Ball

The History of Counting by Denise Schmandt-Besserat

Introduction to Tessellations by Jill Britton

The Man Who Counted: A Collection of Mathematical Adventures by Malba Tahan

Material World by Peter Menzel

Math by Kids! edited by Susan Richman

Math Curse by Jon Scieszka

Math Dictionary for Kids: The Essential Guide to Math Terms, Strategies, and Tables by Theresa Fitzgerald

Math Doesn't Suck and *Kiss My Math* by Danica McKellar

Math for Smarty Pants or *The 'I Hate Math' Book* by Marilyn Burns

Math Games and Activities from Around the World and other books by Claudia Zaslavsky

Math Olympiad Contest Problems by George Lenchner

Math on Call: A Mathematics Handbook by Andrew Kaplan et al.

Math Without Words by James Tanton

Mathematicians Are People, Too (and *Volume 2*) by Luetta and Wilbert Reimer

Murderous Maths series by Kjartan Poskitt

The Number Devil: A Mathematical Adventure by Hans Magnus Enzensberger

The Phantom Tollbooth by Norton Juster

Puzzlegrams and *More Puzzlegrams* compiled by Pentagram

Sam Loyd's Book of Tangrams by Sam Loyd

The Secret Life of Math and others by Ann McCallum

Sideways Arithmetic from Wayside School and *More Sideways Arithmetic* by Louis Sachar

String, Straight-edge & Shadow: The Story of Geometry by Julia E. Diggins

This Is Not a Math Book by Anna Weltman

The Wonderful World of Mathematics by Lancelot Hogben

Teen to Adult

Many of the above, plus:

All the Math You'll Ever Need by Steve Slavin

The Art and Craft of Problem Solving by Paul Zeitz

Calculus Made Easy by Silvanus P. Thompson and Martin Gardner

The Cartoon Guide to Statistics and others by Larry Gonick

The Colossal Book of Mathematics: Classic Puzzles, Paradoxes, and Problems and other books by Martin Gardner

The Complete How to Figure It by Darrell Huff

Crocheting Adventures with Hyperbolic Planes by Daina Taimina

Flatland by Edwin A. Abbott

Games with Pencil and Paper by Eric Solomon

Geometry, Relativity and the Fourth Dimension by Rudolf v. B. Rucker

Hot X: Algebra Exposed and *Girls Get Curves* by Danica McKellar

How to Lie with Statistics by Darrell Huff

How Not to Be Wrong: The Power of Mathematical Thinking by Jordan Ellenberg

How to Solve It by George Polya

Innumeracy: Mathematical Illiteracy and Its Consequences and *A Mathematician Reads the Newspaper* by John Allen Paulos

Invent Your Own Computer Games with Python by Al Sweigart, also available for free download at InventWithPython.com

The Joy of Mathematics and other books by Theoni Pappas

The Joy of x: A Guided Tour of Math, from One to Infinity and other books by Steven Strogatz

The Language of Mathematics: Making the Invisible Visible and other books by Keith Devlin

Lateral Thinking Puzzlers by Paul Sloane

Magical Mathematics: The Mathematical Ideas That Animate Great Magic Tricks by Persi Diaconis and Ron Graham

The Manga Guide to Calculus by Hiroyuki Kojima and Shin Togami

Math Girls by Hiroshi Yuki

Math Jokes 4 Mathy Folks by G. Patrick Vennebush

Mathematical Circles: Russian Experience by Dmitri Fomin et al.

Mathematician's Delight by W. Sawyer

Mathematics: A Human Endeavor by Harold R. Jacobs

Mathematics for the Nonmathematician by Morris Kline

Measurement by Paul Lockhart

The Moscow Puzzles: 359 Mathematical Recreations by Boris A. Kordemsky

Naked Statistics: Stripping the Dread from the Data by Charles Wheelan

The Number Mysteries: A Mathematical Odyssey through Everyday Life and other books by Marcus du Sautoy

A Passion for Mathematics and other books by Clifford A. Pickover

The Princeton Companion to Mathematics by Timothy Gowers et al.

Prisoner's Dilemma by William Poundstone

Problem Solving Through Recreational Mathematics by Bonnie Averbach and Orin Chein

Prof. E. McSquared's Calculus Primer: Expanded Intergalactic Version by Howard Swann and John Johnson

Professor Stewart's Hoard of Mathematical Treasures and other books by Ian Stewart

Relativity in Illustrations by Jacob T. Schwarz

Ruler and Compass: Practical Geometric Constructions by Andrew Sutton

The Signal and the Noise: Why So Many Predictions Fail—but Some Don't by Nate Silver

Solve This: Math Activities for Students and Clubs by James Tanton

Standard Deviations: Flawed Assumptions, Tortured Data, and Other Ways to Lie with Statistics by Gary Smith

Statistics Done Wrong: The Woefully Complete Guide by Alex Reinhart

Taxicab Geometry: An Adventure in Non-Euclidean Geometry by Eugene F. Krause

Thinking Mathematically by John Mason

The Visual Guide to Extra Dimensions by Chris McMullen

What Is the Name of This Book? and other collections of logic puzzles by Raymond Smullyan

Math History and Biographies

Ada's Algorithm: How Lord Byron's Daughter Ada Lovelace Launched the Digital Age by James Essinger

Adventures of a Mathematician by S. M. Ulam

Agnesi to Zeno: Over 100 Vignettes from the History of Math by Sanderson Smith

A Beautiful Mind by Sylvia Nasar

The Code Book: The Science of Secrecy from Ancient Egypt to Quantum Cryptography by Simon Singh

Count Like an Egyptian: A Hands-on Introduction to Ancient Mathematics by David Reimer

Descartes: A Biography by Desmond M. Clarke

"e": The Story of a Number by Eli Maor

Einstein: His Life and Universe by Walter Isaacson

Euler: The Master of Us All by William Dunham

Euler's Gem: The Polyhedron Formula and the Birth of Topology by David S. Richeson

Famous Problems and Their Mathematicians by Art Johnson

Fermat's Enigma: The Epic Quest to Solve the World's Greatest Mathematical Problem by Simon Singh

Gödel, Escher, Bach: An Eternal Golden Braid by Douglas R. Hofstadter

Hilbert by Constance Reid

Historical Connections in Mathematics by Luetta and Wilbert Reimer

The Honors Class: Hilbert's Problems and Their Solvers by Benjamin Yandell

I Want to Be a Mathematician: An Automathography in Three Parts by Paul R. Halmos

In Code: A Mathematical Journey by Sarah Flannery

John Von Neumann: The Scientific Genius Who Pioneered the Modern Computer, Game Theory, Nuclear Deterrence, and Much More by Norman MacRae

Journey through Genius and other books by William Dunham

King of Infinite Space: Donald Coxeter, the Man Who Saved Geometry by Siobhan Roberts

Leibniz: An Intellectual Biography by Maria Rosa Antognazza

The Man Who Knew Infinity: A Life of the Genius Ramanujan by Robert Kanigel

The Math Book: From Pythagoras to the 57th Dimension, 250 Milestones in the History of Mathematics by Clifford A. Pickover

Math Equals by Teri Perl

Math through Children's Literature: Making the NCTM Standards Come Alive by Kathryn L. Braddon et al.

Math through the Ages: A Gentle History for Teachers and Others by William P. Berlinghoff

Mathematics: From the Birth of Numbers by Jan Gullberg

Mathematics Frontiers and other books in the *Pioneers in Mathematics* series by Michael J. Bradley

The Mathmen by Leon Terry

Men of Mathematics by Eric Temple Bell

The Music of the Primes: Searching to Solve the Greatest Mystery in Mathematics by Marcus du Sautoy

My Brain Is Open: The Mathematical Journeys of Paul Erdos by Bruce Schechter

Never at Rest: A Biography of Isaac Newton by Richard S. Westfall

Of Men and Numbers: The Story of the Great Mathematicians by Jane Muir

The Poincaré Conjecture: In Search of the Shape of the Universe by Donal O'Shea

Prime Obsession: Bernhard Riemann and the Greatest Unsolved Problem in Mathematics by John Derbyshire

Remarkable Mathematicians: From Euler to von Neumann by Ioan James

Unknown Quantity: A Real and Imaginary History of Algebra by John Derbyshire

Women and Numbers by Teri Perl and Analee Nunan

Women in Mathematics by Lynn M. Osen

The World of Mathematics: A Four-Volume Set by James R. Newman

...And there are plenty more where these came from, enough to keep you exploring mathematics for a lifetime.

Math Resources on the Internet

THE INTERNET OVERFLOWS WITH A wide-ranging assortment of math websites. Here are some of my favorites, both schoolish math and fun stuff. These links and more are available on my website, where I will add new goodies as I find the time. *http://denisegaskins.com/internet-math-resources*

All the website links in this book were checked in December 2015, and I do my best to keep my blog list up to date, but the Internet is volatile. If a website disappears, you can run a browser search for the author's name or article title. Or try entering the web address at the Internet Archive Wayback Machine. *http://archive.org/web/web.php*

For Parents and Teachers

ADDING IT UP, HELPING CHILDREN LEARN MATHEMATICS: An overview of research about elementary school arithmetic and how to teach it, free for downloading or reading online.
http://www.nap.edu/openbook.php?record_id=9822&page=71

AND 'RITHMETIC: The Sudbury Valley School approach to math education, by Daniel Greenberg.
https://www.scribd.com/doc/14389275/And-Rithmetic-by-Daniel-Greenberg

ART OF PROBLEM SOLVING MATH ARTICLES: A variety of topics about teaching and learning math.
http://artofproblemsolving.com/articles

CLOTHESLINE MATH: Harness the power of the number line to build understanding from early elementary school to high school.
http://clotheslinemath.com

DENISEGASKINS.COM: My "Let's Play Math!" blog of games, teaching tips, and resource pages. For instance, check out my Word Problems from Literature series.
http://denisegaskins.com
http://denisegaskins.com/2010/04/26/word-problems-from-literature

EDUCATION UNBOXED: Videos by homeschooling mom Rosie showing how to play with elementary math using Cuisenaire rods and other hands-on tools.
http://www.educationunboxed.com

ELEMENTS OF MATH: Steven Strogatz's blog post series from *The New York Times*. His

Stay Safe

Many excellent interactive math websites require Java or Adobe Flash. Unfortunately, both programs can also be used by hackers to break into your computer or do other nasty stuff. Make sure you have the most recent versions of each program. Keep your security settings up to date. In order to use a Java-based Internet app, you will need to add that website to your computer's Java Exception Site List.

http://java.com
http://java.com/en/download/faq/exception_sitelist.xml
http://www.adobe.com/products/flashplayer.html

"Me, Myself and Math" series is also worth reading.
http://topics.nytimes.com/top/opinion/series/steven_strogatz_on_the_elements_of_math/index.html
http://opinionator.blogs.nytimes.com/category/me-myself-and-math/

EVER WONDER WHAT THEY'D NOTICE? (IF ONLY SOMEONE WOULD ASK): Annie Fetter's classic presentation on talking with kids about math.
https://youtu.be/a-Fth6sOaRA

GLOBAL STRATEGY STAGE ASSESSMENT (GLoSS): A one-on-one test of mathematical understanding. You read a question, give your child time to think, and then compare what he or she says to the range of possible responses. Be sure to read the Additional Information about Gloss (PDF) before interviewing your student.
http://www.nzmaths.co.nz/gloss-forms?parent_nod
http://www.nzmaths.co.nz/sites/default/files/Numeracy/GloSS/GloSS_Additional_Information.pdf

THE HARMFUL EFFECTS OF "CARRYING" AND "BORROWING" (PDF): Teaching abstract rules too soon can damage children's intuition about numbers.
https://sites.google.com/site/constancekamii/articles-available-for-printing/The_Harmful_Effects_of_Carrying_and_Borrowing_%282009%29.pdf

HELPING A STRUGGLING MATH STUDENT: A 14-part series at Angelicscalliwags blog, full of activities and encouragement. Scroll to the bottom to read the posts in the order they were published.
http://angelicscalliwags.com/category/helping-a-struggling-maths-student

HOW TO THINK LIKE A SCHOOL MATH GENIUS: James Tanton's series of videos about five key principles for mathematical thinking.
http://www.jamestanton.com/?p=1097

KENKEN FOR TEACHERS: A fantastic way to practice arithmetic.
http://www.kenkenpuzzle.com/teachers/classroom

LIVING MATH: Julie Brennan's amazing website features the most extensive lists of living math books anywhere, plus articles about math, book and resource reviews, and lesson plans. Brennan also moderates the Yahoo group, Living Math Forum.
http://livingmath.net
http://groups.yahoo.com/group/LivingMathForum

MATH BY KIDS!: A 78-page workbook of original math problems (including solutions) created by homeschooled students aged four to seventeen, edited by Susan Richman. If this store link stops working, go to the Pennsylvania Homeschoolers website and click around until you find the book.
https://pahomeschoolers.c9.ixsecure.com/oscommerce-2.3.3/catalog/product_info.php? products_id=42
http://www.pahomeschoolers.com

MATH JOURNALS BOOST REAL LEARNING (PDF): An article by Marilyn Burns. Math journals "help students stretch their thinking and make sense of problems," and they can help teachers evaluate student progress.
http://www.coach4math.com/wp-content/uploads/2010/03/Math-Journals-Boost-Real-Learning-Article.pdf

MATH REASONING INVENTORY: Find out how much your elementary or middle school students understand about math. You do not have to sign up for an account to access the resources. Before doing the oral assessment testing, be sure to read the Reasoning Strategy PDF Files that outline what the assessment is looking for and watch the videos to see what sort of answers to expect.
https://mathreasoninginventory.com
https://mathreasoninginventory.com/Home/Resources

MATH TALKS: Fawn Nguyen's collection of questions that spark thinking about math, with sample student answers and tips for the teacher.
http://www.mathtalks.net

MODERN MATH FOR ELEMENTARY SCHOOLERS (PDF): Downloadable Creative Commons (CC BY-NC-SA 3.0) book by Oleg Gleizer with more than two hundred puzzles about numbers, geometry, infinity, and more.
http://old.naturalmath.com/DeltaStreamMedia/OlegGleizerModernMathematics_12_2011.pdf

MOEBIUS NOODLES: "Adventurous math for the playground crowd." Plenty of ideas for sharing rich math experiences with your children.
http://www.moebiusnoodles.com

NIX THE TRICKS: Tina Cardone's free guide explains how mnemonic tricks and shortcuts hinder student understanding of math. Learn which phrases to avoid and what to use in their place.
http://nixthetricks.com

PROBLEM SOLVING STRATEGIES: Finlay McQuade's tips for teaching your students to solve math problems.
http://pred.boun.edu.tr/ps

RELATIONAL UNDERSTANDING AND INSTRUMENTAL UNDERSTANDING (PDF): The original article by Richard Skemp on the two ways of understanding mathematics.
http://math.coe.uga.edu/olive/EMAT3500f08/instrumental-relational.pdf

SNAP—SCAFFOLDING FOR NUMERICAL SYNAPSES: Montessori-influenced activities by Sheryl Morris. Help preschool children find numbers, their related patterns, and geometric shapes in the world all around them.
http://www.snap-scaffoldingfornumericalsynapses.com

STANDARDS FOR MATHEMATICAL PRACTICE: The best part of the Common Core Math reform, a summary of what it means to think mathematically from kindergarten to high school.
http://www.corestandards.org/Math/Practice

TALKING MATH WITH YOUR KIDS: Christopher Danielson helps parents support their children's mathematical development.
http://talkingmathwithkids.com

TALKING STICK MATH CIRCLE BLOG: Inspiring stories about children grappling with math concepts, by Rodi Steinig.
http://talkingsticklearningcenter.org/category/math-circle-blog

THE TEACHING OF ARITHMETIC: The Story of an Experiment: In 1929, American school superintendent Louis P. Benezet delayed arithmetic to help students build a foundation in reasoning.
http://wol.ra.phy.cam.ac.uk/sanjoy/benezet/three.html

ULTIMATE LIST OF PRINTABLE MATH MANIPULATIVES & GAMES: A treasure list from Jimmie Lanley, one of my favorite homeschooling bloggers.
http://jimmiescollage.com/2011/04/ultimate-list-of-printable-math-manipulatives-games

UNSCHOOLERS AND MATHEMATICS: Sandra Dodd's collection of stories about children learning math naturally, without being pushed to use textbooks or to drill math facts. Inspiring.
http://sandradodd.com/math

THE WORLD OF MATHEMATICAL REALITY: Catch a vision of mathematical beauty in this video by Paul Lockhart. See also his essay "A Mathematician's Lament" (PDF).
https://youtu.be/V1gT2f3Fe44
https://www.maa.org/external_archive/devlin/LockhartsLament.pdf

WRITING IN MATHEMATICS: Terry Kawas's tips to help students reflect on their learning, deepen their understanding, and make important connections to real-life applications.
http://mathwire.com/writing/writing1.html

YELENA'S HUNDRED CHART POSTER: Printable hundred chart poster and game cards from Moebius Noodles blogger Yelena McManaman.
http://www.moebiusnoodles.com/2013/01/the-hundred-chart-and-game-cards

YOUCUBED: Jo Boaler's website for research-based ways to teach math that can help

discouraged students feel empowered to learn. Also try her free online course for students and their parents: How to Learn Math.
http://www.youcubed.org
http://www.youcubed.org/how-to-learn-math-for-students

Math Adventures for All Ages

ALICE: A downloadable programming system that allows students to learn by creating animated movies and simple video games.
http://www.alice.org/index.php

CODE.ORG: Game-like computer programming tutorials for beginners and beyond.
http://code.org/learn

CODECADEMY: Interactive lessons in a variety of programming languages, along with project ideas and forums for asking questions.
http://www.codecademy.com

CS UNPLUGGED: Learning activities that teach computer science through games and puzzles using cards, string, crayons and lots of running around.
http://csunplugged.org

CUT THE KNOT INTERACTIVE: Alexander Bogomolny's "Mathematics Miscellany and Puzzles," one of my all-time favorite sites.
http://www.cut-the-knot.org

DAILY TREASURE: Solve the logic puzzle to find the hidden gold.
http://4chests.blogspot.com

DON COHEN'S MAP OF CALCULUS FOR YOUNG PEOPLE: Hands-on activities featuring advanced ideas, for students of any age. Check out my introductory blog post Infinite Cake: Don Cohen's Infinite Series for Kids.
http://www.mathman.biz/html/map.html
http://denisegaskins.com/2015/07/02/infinite-cake-don-cohens-infinite-series-for-kids

DOODLING IN MATH: Recreational mathematics and inspirational videos by math-emusician Vi Hart. For newer videos, see her blog ViHart.com.
https://www.khanacademy.org/math/recreational-math/vi-hart

ESTIMATION 180: Andrew Stadel's site for "Building number sense one day at a time." How close can you guess?
http://www.estimation180.com

FAMOUS PROBLEMS IN THE HISTORY OF MATHEMATICS: This site includes problems, paradoxes, and proofs that have inspired mathematicians through the ages, plus links for further exploration.
http://mathforum.org/isaac/mathhist.html

FUN MATHEMATICS LESSONS BY CYNTHIA LANIUS: A variety of topics and investigations.
http://math.rice.edu/~lanius/Lessons

GEOMETRY LESSONS IN THE WALDORF SCHOOL: Freehand Form Drawing and Basic Geometric Construction: (Includes link to free PDF download) The book says "Grades 4 and 5," but Waldorf-style geometry doodling is fun for all ages.
http://www.waldorflibrary.org/books/3/view_bl/113/form-drawing/120/geometry-lessons-in-the-waldorf-school-ebook

GOLDEN SALES PITCH: "There is little evidence to suggest that the golden ratio has any special aesthetic appeal ... When a myth is repeated over and over, it begins to sound like truth."
http://www.sciencenews.org/view/generic/id/8660/title/A_Golden_Sales_Pitch

HISTORY OF MATHEMATICAL GAMES AND RECREATIONS: "The whole history of mathematics is interwoven with mathematical games which have led to the study of many areas of mathematics."
http://www-groups.dcs.st-and.ac.uk/~history/HistTopics/Mathematical_games.html

HOTEL INFINITY: Tova Brown's growing collection of videos that explore advanced math concepts through story-telling.
http://www.hotel-infinity.com

ISLAMIC ART AND GEOMETRIC DESIGN (PDF): Lesson plans from the Metropolitan Museum.
http://www.metmuseum.org/~/media/Files/Learn/For Educators/Publications for Educators/Islamic_Art_and_Geometric_Design.pdf

JILL BRITTON'S HOME PAGE: A wealth of links and resources for playing with topology, symmetry, tessellations, and polyhedra.
http://britton.disted.camosun.bc.ca/home.htm

MATH HOMBRE GAMES: Links to math games on GVSU math professor John Golden's blog, games on other people's blogs, and more games all over the Internet.
http://bit.ly/mhGames

MATH IS FUN: A mathematical smorgasbord of lessons, definitions, puzzles, and games.
http://www.mathsisfun.com/index.htm

MATH MUNCH: A weekly digest of delicious math activities, projects, artwork, and games from around the Internet.
http://mathmunch.org

MATH PICKLE: Gordon Hamilton offers challenging printable games/puzzles for K–12 students. Can your kids solve the $1,000,000 problems?
http://www.mathpickle.com

NATIONAL LIBRARY OF VIRTUAL MANIPULATIVES: A treasure-chest of virtual hands-on math. Includes links to material for all ages and topics, pre-K through 12th grade.
http://nlvm.usu.edu/en/nav/vlibrary.html

NRICH.MATHS.ORG: A wonderful source of math puzzles and activities for all ages, with a theme that changes each month. Hints available, and solutions for past problems.
http://nrich.maths.org/public/index.php

ORIGAMI AND MATH: David Eppstein's Geometry Junkyard links to a slew of origami articles and projects.
http://www.ics.uci.edu/~eppstein/junkyard/origami.html

ORIGAMI INSTRUCTIONS: You can make a variety of polyhedra from Sonobe modules. See also Wikipedia: Sonobe.
http://www.origami-instructions.com/modular-sonobe-unit.html
http://en.wikipedia.org/wiki/Sonobe

PAGAT.COM: Pagat is a wonderful collection of card game rules and variations from around the world.
http://www.pagat.com

PASCAL'S TRIANGLE: Lessons and links for all grade levels. See also, "All You Ever Wanted to Know about Pascal's Triangle."
http://mathforum.org/workshops/usi/pascal
http://ptri1.tripod.com

PROBLEM SOLVING ISLAND: A variety of puzzles, from the book *Thinking Mathematically* and other sources, plus problem-solving tips and sample student journal entries.
http://www.math.grin.edu/~rebelsky/ProblemSolving/index.html

QUARTO: A strategy game to play online. Can you get four pieces in a row?
http://quarto.mygamesonline.org/en

RECREATIONAL MATHEMATICS AT WOLFRAM MATHWORLD: Games, art, humor, and more.
http://mathworld.wolfram.com/topics/RecreationalMathematics.html

RUSH HOUR ONLINE: "Your goal is to drive your red car out of the playing grid and escape to freedom."
http://www.puzzles.com/products/RushHour/RHfromMarkRiedel/Jam.html

SCRATCH: A programming language developed at MIT that makes it easy for students to create interactive stories, animations, games, music, and art—and share those creations on the web.
http://scratch.mit.edu

SET DAILY PUZZLE: A visual logic puzzle for all ages.
http://www.setgame.com/set/puzzle_frame.htm

TIM'S INTERACTIVE PUZZLE SOLUTION CENTER: A collection of "famous and other curious brain teasers," some relatively easy and some quite challenging.
http://sakharov.net/puzzle

UNIVERSCALE: Compare and understand the relative size of the full range of known objects in our universe.
http://www.nikon.com/about/feelnikon/universcale

VISUAL PATTERNS: Fawn Nguyen's algebraic reasoning puzzles. Pick any design and practice recognizing, describing, and predicting the pattern.
http://www.visualpatterns.org

WHICH ONE DOESN'T BELONG? PUZZLERS: Mary Bourassa's thought-provoking puzzles will challenge math teachers and students alike. Can you identify which item doesn't belong and explain why?
http://wodb.ca/index.html

WOULD YOU RATHER? MATH: John Stevens's decision-making challenge. "Asking students to choose their own path and justify it."
http://www.wyrmath.com

Elementary and Middle School Fun Stuff

AMBLEWEB FUNCTION MACHINE: Choose the type of problem you want to guess, or go random for more challenge. My math club kids love function machines.
http://www.amblesideprimary.com/ambleweb/mentalmaths/functionmachines.html

BEDTIME MATH: Laura Overdeck's daily math problem (with answers) at three levels of difficulty, approximately preschool to upper-elementary level.
http://bedtimemathproblem.org

DONALD DUCK IN MATHMAGIC LAND: The classic math cartoon from Walt Disney, now free on YouTube.
https://youtu.be/U_ZHsk0-eF0

DRAGONBOX APPS: Playful math apps that use puzzles to teach the basic principles of numbers, algebra, and geometry.
http://dragonbox.com

EGYPTIAN MATH: Mark Millmore introduces students to Egyptian numerals and hieroglyph mathematics.
http://www.eyelid.co.uk/numbers.htm

ERATOSTHENES' SIEVE: Click on any number, and all of its multiples (except the number itself) will disappear from the chart.
http://www.hbmeyer.de/eratosiv.htm

FIBONACCI NUMBERS AND NATURE: Find out all about his famous rabbits, and about honeybees, seashells, pinecones, and more from Ron Knott.
http://www.maths.surrey.ac.uk/hosted-sites/R.Knott/Fibonacci/fibnat.html

GRAPH MOLE AND LINE GEM: Two coordinate graphing. games by Sulan Dun
http://funbasedlearning.com/algebra

GRAPHING STORIES: Dan Meyer's fifteen-second videos with action for students to graph. How does the height, air pressure, etc. change with time?
http://graphingstories.com

HANDS-ON EQUATIONS: These apps take a step-by-step approach to solving simple (linear) algebra equations.
http://www.borenson.com/tabid/1594/Default.aspx

HEAD HUNTERS GAME: A bloody fun game for the Viking in all of us. If you enjoy that one, try the other math tricks and games at Murderous Maths.
http://www.murderousmaths.co.uk/games/headhunt/headhunt.htm
http://www.murderousmaths.co.uk

Logic-Grid Brain Teasers: I love logic grid problems, and Braingle offers thirty-four pages of them. See also: Math Brain Teasers.
http://www.braingle.com/Logic-Grid.html
http://www.braingle.com/Math.html

Math Cats: Math explorations, crafts, homemade manipulatives, and cats.
http://www.mathcats.com

Math Playground: Colleen King shares a variety of math games that make students think—not just number drill.
http://www.mathplayground.com

Math Wire: Activities and games for elementary students by Terry Kawas. Check out the Hundred Chart Logic Puzzles.
http://mathwire.com
http://www.mathwire.com/problemsolving/hblogic.html

MegaPenny Project: How many does it take to pile up a ton of pennies?
http://www.kokogiak.com/megapenny

Multiplication, An Adventure in Number Sense: Explore the multiplication table and discover some interesting things about how numbers work.
https://web.archive.org/web/20070107073522/http:/www.naturalmath.com/mult/mult1.html

Multiplication Models: How many different ways can you think of to look at multiplication?
https://web.archive.org/web/20150315214853/http:/www.naturalmath.com/multmodels/index.php

One is one ... or is it?: One bag of apples, one apple, one slice of apple—which of these is one unit? Video by Christopher Danielson.
https://youtu.be/EtclcWGG7WQ

Suzanne's Math Lessons: Activities and projects for upper-elementary and middle school, collected by Suzanne Alejandre.
http://mathforum.org/alejandre/index.html

Taxicab Treasure Hunt: A game based on the non-Euclidean geometry of city streets.
http://www.learner.org/teacherslab/math/geometry/shape/taxicab/index.html

Thinking Blocks: Learn to solve word problems by modeling them with interactive virtual blocks. A visual approach to thinking things through.
http://www.thinkingblocks.com

ThinkQuest History of Mathematics: Brief overview of math history, with biographies of influential mathematicians and short online quizzes.
https://web.archive.org/web/20070315145728/http:/library.thinkquest.org/4116/History/history.htm

Who Was Fibonacci?: "A brief biographical sketch of Fibonacci, his life, times and mathematical achievements" by Ron Knott.
http://www.maths.surrey.ac.uk/hosted-sites/R.Knott/Fibonacci/fibBio.html

WUZZIT TROUBLE: A challenging app that combines an adventure game with mathematical thinking skills, produced by Stanford mathematician Keith Devlin and friends.
http://wuzzit-trouble.com

Worksheets, Lessons, and Full Curriculum

ACCESS MATHS: A collection of math review worksheets and games.
http://www.accessmaths.co.uk

ART OF PROBLEM SOLVING VIDEO LESSONS: For middle school (prealgebra) and up, featuring the ever-entertaining Richard Rusczyk.
http://www.artofproblemsolving.com/videos

COOL MATH: Math lessons for prealgebra, algebra, and precalculus, plus math games and other activities.
http://www.coolmath.com

CORBETTMATHS 5-A-DAY: Review elementary and middle school math skills with daily practice problem sets.
http://corbettmaths.com/5-a-day

DAD'S WORKSHEETS: More than 8,000 worksheets you can print for elementary and middle school math practice.
http://www.dadsworksheets.com

DONNA YOUNG'S MATH PAGES: Worksheets, charts, drill pages, fraction manipulatives, triangular flashcards, and more.
http://donnayoung.org/math

FRAYER MODEL PRINTABLE: A graphic organizer designed to provide for a thorough understanding of new vocabulary words.
http://www.worksheetworks.com/miscellanea/graphic-organizers/frayer.html

FREE MATH WORKSHEETS FROM HOMESCHOOLMATH.NET: A variety of worksheets from Maria Miller, author of the *Math Mammoth* books, with links at the bottom of the page for more freebies.
http://www.homeschoolmath.net/worksheets

FREE PRINTABLES FROM TABLETOP ACADEMY PRESS: Hundred charts, game boards, and graph paper to accompany my *Math You Can Play* series.
http://tabletopacademy.net/playful-math-books/free-printables

INCOMPETECH: Free online graph paper PDFs galore for any math or science project.
http://incompetech.com/graphpaper

JUMP MATH: A step-by-step math curriculum for grades 1–8, great for discouraged students or late bloomers. Register for a free account to download the goodies.
http://www.jumpmath.org

KHAN ACADEMY: Free video lectures and online quizzes.
https://www.khanacademy.org

LIVING MATH HISTORY PLANS: Julie Brennan's curriculum provides a multi-level structure for home educating or afterschooling families to study math through history and related math topics in context.

http://www.livingmath.net/LessonPlans/LessonPlanInformation/tabid/1002/Default.aspx

MATH AS A SECOND LANGUAGE: Herb Gross teaches elementary arithmetic by building on students' intuition about spoken language. Companion videos for teachers at YouTube.

http://www.lovemath.org/index.html
https://youtu.be/QFFReY6lS68?list=PLWwhzNbWxQjvu7zDZhLytz9iUXI8IUN3D

MATH CACHING: Students solve mathematical problems to find hidden "boxes" on the Internet. Each box reveals clues to the location of the next one. Levels range from prealgebra to trigonometry.

http://mathbits.com/caching/MathCacheDirectionsOpen.html

THE MATH PAGE: Lawrence Spector's interactive lessons in arithmetic, algebra, and assorted other topics.

http://www.themathpage.com/index.html

MATH WORKSHEET SITE: Scott Bryce's online generator for basic math worksheets, including 1–100 or 0–99 charts. They also offer a subscription service with a wider choice of topics.

http://themathworksheetsite.com

MATHEMATICS ENHANCEMENT PROGRAMME (MEP): A full curriculum for kindergarten through high school, with so many resources that it's easy to get lost. If you have questions, ask at the MEP Homeschoolers Forum on Yahoo.

http://www.cimt.plymouth.ac.uk/projects/mep/default.htm
http://groups.yahoo.com/groups/mep-homeschoolers

NRICH CURRICULUM MAPS FOR PRIMARY (STAGES 1–2, GRADES 1–5) AND SECONDARY (STAGES 3–5, GRADES 6–12): Resources which will help you embed problem solving into your curriculum.

http://nrich.maths.org/8935
http://nrich.maths.org/8517

PROBLEM BASED CURRICULUM MAPS: Geoff Krall has collected many free math activities and lessons, sorted by grade level and arranged to flow in a natural progression.

http://emergentmath.com/my-problem-based-curriculum-maps

SUCH A THING AS FREE: Could you put together a full year's worth of math from free resources on the Internet? John Golden offers a wealth of links.

http://mathhombre.blogspot.com/2014/10/such-thing-as-free.html

USING THE REKENREK AS A VISUAL MODEL FOR STRATEGIC REASONING IN MATHEMATICS (PDF): Number sense lessons for the rekenrek by Barbara Blanke. Check out the number rack browser app, too.

http://bridges1.mathlearningcenter.org/media/Rekenrek_0308.pdf
http://www.mathlearningcenter.org/web-apps/number-rack/

Algebra and Beyond

ACTIVE CALCULUS: A free, open-source calculus textbook with activities. See also Screencasts for Active Calculus.
http://scholarworks.gvsu.edu/books/10
https://opencalculus.wordpress.com/2015/08/25/screencasts-for-active-calculus

ADJECTIVENOUNMATH.COM: Herb Gross's high school site, with courses on arithmetic, algebra, and calculus. Many of the videos are old-fashioned and slow, but the teacher builds on student intuition to promote understanding better than many of the flashy new sites I've seen.
http://adjectivenounmath.com/index.html

ALCUMUS: Art of Problem Solving's innovative online learning system adjusts to student performance to deliver appropriate problems and lessons.
http://www.artofproblemsolving.com/alcumus

BETTER EXPLAINED: Kalid Azad's intuitive, often visual, explanations of high school math topics.
http://betterexplained.com

BAYESIAN STATISTICS FOR DUMMIES: Kevin Boone's introduction to statistical questions that deal with conditional probabilities. See also the *New York Times* article "The Odds, Continually Updated."
http://www.kevinboone.net/bayes.html
http://www.nytimes.com/2014/09/30/science/the-odds-continually-updated.html

CALCULUS CONCEPTS AND APPLICATIONS: A complete set of student-centered activities for a year-long Calculus I and Calculus II sequence.
http://www.iblcalculus.com/home

DESMOS GRAPHING CALCULATOR: Explore the relationships between equations and shapes, and try your hands at some of the Daily Desmos blog challenges.
https://www.desmos.com
http://dailydesmos.com

DISCOVERING THE ART OF MATHEMATICS: Activity-based math from a liberal-arts approach.
https://www.artofmathematics.org/books

DISCOVERING TRIGONOMETRY: David Eisenberg's basic introduction to trigonometry, starting with sticks and shadows.
http://catcode.com/trig/index.html

EUCLID'S ELEMENTS: David E. Joyce brings the text of Euclid's thirteen books to life with Java applets. Also see An Introduction to the Works of Euclid.
http://aleph0.clarku.edu/~djoyce/java/elements/toc.html
http://www.obkb.com/dcljr/euclid.html

EUCLID IN COLORFUL DIAGRAMS: Oliver Byrne's innovative, pictorial version of the first six books of the Elements of Euclid.
https://www.math.ubc.ca/~cass/Euclid/byrne.html

FLATLAND: Edwin Abbott's "Romance of Many Dimensions."
http://www.ibiblio.org/eldritch/eaa/FL.HTM

G'DAY MATH COURSES: James Tanton unlocks the simplicity of seemingly complex ideas about arithmetic, algebra, probability, and more.
http://gdaymath.com/courses

GALLERY OF DATA VISUALIZATION: Michael Friendly's collection of the world's best and worst statistical graphs.
http://www.datavis.ca/gallery/index.php

GEOGEBRA: Download software for playing with geometry and algebra, and the website offers a wealth of user-created instructional materials.
http://www.geogebra.org/cms

GREEN TEA PRESS: Free statistics and computer science books by Allen Downey.
http://greenteapress.com/wp

HOW TO READ MATHEMATICS: "A math article usually tells only a small piece of a much larger and longer story." Learn to read between the lines.
http://web.stonehill.edu/compsci/History_Math/math-read.htm

HOW TO THINK LIKE A SCHOOL MATH GENIUS: James Tanton's series of videos about five key principles for mathematical thinking for students approaching high school math.
http://www.jamestanton.com/?p=1097

INTERACTIVE MATHEMATICS: Murray Bourne's interactive apps let you explore math and get a better understanding of what it all means.
http://www.intmath.com

INTRODUCTION TO MATHEMATICAL THINKING: Keith Devlin's free online course on language and logic, reasoning and proof.
https://www.coursera.org/course/maththink

INVENT YOUR OWN COMPUTER GAMES WITH PYTHON: In each chapter, Al Sweigart gives your student the complete source code for a new game, then teaches programming concepts from the example.
http://inventwithpython.com

JULIA ROBINSON MATH FESTIVAL: Question sets from a collaborative, non-competitive celebration of thought-provoking problems.
http://jrmf.org/problems.php

KARL'S CALCULUS: Karl Hahn has a creative way of explaining the ideas of calculus. Includes sample problems.
http://web.archive.org/web/20140517212513/http:/karlscalculus.org

LA HABRA HIGH SCHOOL'S MATH HISTORY TIMELINE: Math discoveries, publications, and other tidbits from paleolithic number bones to the present.
http://web.archive.org/web/20080509062108/http://lahabra.seniorhigh.net/pages/teachers/pages/math/timeline/MpreAndAncient.html

LET'S PLAY ANCIENT GREEK GEOMETRY: Nico Disseldorp's online game of complet-

ing Euclidean geometry construction puzzles in a certain number of moves.
http://sciencevsmagic.net/geo

MacTutor History of Mathematics Archive: My favorite place to begin any foray into math history.
http://www-history.mcs.st-and.ac.uk

Mathematical Problems of David Hilbert: With a link to Hilbert's 1900 address to the International Congress of Mathematicians in Paris, surely the most influential speech ever given about mathematics. Wolfram MathWorld has an annotated list of all twenty-three problems.
http://aleph0.clarku.edu/~djoyce/hilbert
http://mathworld.wolfram.com/HilbertsProblems.html

Mathematical Reasoning: Writing and Proof: Ted Sundstrom's online textbook for high school students and adults who want to develop the ability to think more abstractly.
http://scholarworks.gvsu.edu/books/9

Median by Don Steward: A collection of activities and exercises for middle school and high school students.
http://donsteward.blogspot.co.uk

Muslim Rule and Compass: The Magic of Islamic Geometric Design: An article by Alex Bellos, with instructions for constructing a beautiful geometric pattern.
http://www.theguardian.com/science/alexs-adventures-in-numberland/2015/feb/10/
muslim-rule-and-compass-the-magic-of-islamic-geometric-design

A New Algebra: Henri Picciotto offers a selection of interesting activities for algebra students.
http://www.mathedpage.org/new-algebra/new-algebra.html

Non-Euclid: Joel Castellanos's website for exploring the mind-blowingly weird world of hyperbolic geometry. See also the hyperbolic art of M. C. Escher.
http://cs.unm.edu/~joel/NonEuclid/NonEuclid.html
http://www.josleys.com/show_gallery.php?galid=325

Phillips Exeter Academy Math: An entire high school curriculum made up only of problems.
http://www.exeter.edu/academics/72_6539.aspx

Project Euler: A list of programming challenges for advanced students.
http://projecteuler.net/index.php?section=problems

Proofs Without Words: I love these.
http://usamts.org/Gallery/G_Gallery.php

Purplemath: Elizabeth Stapel's explanations for prealgebra and algebra topics. When your textbook just doesn't make sense, look here for help.
http://www.purplemath.com/modules/index.htm

Spurious Correlations: Tyler Vigen takes statistical humor to new heights.
http://www.tylervigen.com

STATISTICS EVERY WRITER SHOULD KNOW: Robert Niles's introductory statistics tutorial for math-phobic journalists.
http://www.robertniles.com/stats

STATS WITHOUT TEARS: Stan Brown's free online statistics textbook.
http://brownmath.com/swt

STELLA'S STUNNERS: More than 600 non-routine mathematics problems ranging from simple visual puzzles requiring no specific mathematical background, to problems that use the content of prealgebra up through precalculus.
http://www.ohiorc.org/for/math/stella

TAXICAB GEOMETRY INVESTIGATION (PDF): A 19-page printable guiding students as they investigate and make their own discoveries about taxicab geometry. For more advanced taxicab math, see TaxicabGeometry.net.
http://faculty.cord.edu/andersod/TaxicabWorksheets.pdf
http://taxicabgeometry.net

THINKING MATHEMATICS VIDEOS: James Tanton's common-sense approach to high school mathematics. See also his Puzzles and Cool Math page.
http://www.jamestanton.com/?cat=6
http://www.jamestanton.com/?cat=4

TIPS FOR ALL YOUR MATH COURSES: Articles by Stan Brown about how to succeed as a math student, how to use a graphing calculator, what it means to "show your work," and other topics from algebra, trig, calculus, and statistics.
http://brownmath.com/stfa

TRIG WITHOUT TEARS: "Or, How to Remember Trigonometric Identities." How to learn and understand trig without memorizing a gazillion identities. Check out the author's other mathematics articles, too.
http://brownmath.com/twt

VIRTUAL MATH LAB: Algebra tutorials from West Texas A&M University. Includes practice tests.
http://www.wtamu.edu/academic/anns/mps/math/mathlab

WHAT'S SPECIAL ABOUT THIS NUMBER?: Erich Friedman serves up distinctive facts about several numbers, 0–9999 the last time I looked.
http://www2.stetson.edu/~efriedma/numbers.html

Math Contests

Math contests can be a great source of thought-provoking problems, even for students who dislike competition. Most of these require a registration fee, and most do not accept individual registrations. Organize teams through your school or homeschool group.

MATH KANGAROO: International contest for all grade levels. Students compete individually at their own schools, and then scores are compared nationally. Awards given at school and national levels.
http://www.aksf.org

MATHEMATICAL OLYMPIADS FOR ELEMENTARY AND MIDDLE SCHOOLS: International elementary (grades 4–6) and middle school (grades 6–8) levels. Five monthly contests during the school year. Students compete individually in their own schools or homeschool groups—with certificates for everyone and a top-scorer trophy—and then scores are compared nationally for additional awards.
http://www.moems.org/index.htm

THE MATH LEAGUE: International contest for fourth grade through high school levels. Students compete individually at their own schools, and then scores are compared nationally. Students may take the test on paper or online.
http://mathleague.com

MATHCOUNTS: U.S. middle school teams (grades 6–8). Students compete individually at the school level. Each school or homeschool group may send a team of four students to a regional competition, with the top teams progressing to state and national contests (travel required). Study resources available through the Math-Counts website and at the following links:
http://mathcounts.org

♦ MATHCOUNTS DRILLS BY ELIAS SAAB: Tough online practice problems for Math-Counts preparation, or simply to see if you can handle the challenge.
http://mathcounts.saab.org/mc.cgi

♦ MATHCOUNTS TOOLBOX (PDF): This is a nine-page summary of the basic facts of elementary math. Go through each page, checking off all the things you know. Then try to learn at least one new math fact per week.
http://www.stjudefw.org/mathclub/pdf/coachkit-toolbox.pdf

♦ THE MATHCOUNTS BIBLE ACCORDING TO MR. DIAZ: "What you must memorize, without excuses and for the rest of your lives (not just for Math Counts)."
http://www.unidata.ucar.edu/staff/russ/mathcounts/diaz.html

PURPLE COMET MATH MEET: International contest for middle school and high school teams. Students work together to solve a set of problems and enter their answers online. Mixed-age teams may choose a non-competitive category. Past-years' contests are available on the website for practice.
http://purplecomet.org

AMERICAN MATHEMATICS COMPETITIONS: U.S. middle school through high school students compete individually at their own schools, and then scores are compared nationally. Awards given at school and national levels. Past tests available through the website for practice.
http://amc.maa.org

MANDLEBROT COMPETITION: International high school students compete individually and in teams of four. Ribbons given to top four scorers at the school level, additional awards at the national level.
http://www.mandelbrot.org

USA MATHEMATICAL TALENT SEARCH: U.S. high school, or advanced middle school individuals—no team required. Free. Students must solve challenging problems and write well-justified solutions. Four rounds per year, five problems per round,

with one month to work each set. Past problem sets available on the website.
http://www.usamts.org

Forums Where You Can Ask for Help

ART OF PROBLEM SOLVING FORUM: For middle school and older students, focusing on the puzzling challenge problems found in math competitions.
http://www.artofproblemsolving.com/community

ASK DR. MATH: Browse the archives of the Math Forum. If you can't find what you are looking for, ask a new question by email.
http://mathforum.org/dr.math

FREE MATH HELP FORUM: Help and advice on topics from arithmetic to differential equations.
http://www.freemathhelp.com/forum/forum.php

MATH HELP FORUM: Help for algebra and beyond.
http://mathhelpforum.com/math-help-forum.php

PURPLEMATH FORUMS: "Helping students gain understanding and self-confidence in algebra" and plenty of other high school math topics.
http://www.purplemath.com/learning/index.php

S.O.S. CYBERBOARD: A topical help forum for high school and college-level mathematics, engineering, computer science, and more.
http://www.sosmath.com/CBB/index.php

Appendix C

Answers to Sample Problems

[1] If you take away one-fourth

The answer is twenty or sixty, depending on how you interpreted the question. When you "take away one-fourth," are you taking that portion as your share, or are you subtracting it and keeping the other three-fourths? If you think of "take away" as subtraction, as if you are throwing that portion away, then you get my answer:

$$(1 - \tfrac{1}{4})\,N + 2 = 17$$
$$\tfrac{3}{4} \times N = 15$$
$$N = 20$$

If you take the portion as your share, like taking a large piece of pizza, you will find my daughter's answer:

$$\tfrac{1}{4} \times N + 2 = 17$$
$$\tfrac{1}{4} \times N = 15$$
$$N = 60$$

[2] If you multiply me by myself

Work backward. There are 100 pennies in a dollar, so half that would be fifty. Then subtract the one that was added, which gives forty-nine. The secret number times itself must equal forty-nine, so that means the number is seven.

[3] If you divide me by two

To write the whole mess in algebra:

$$(\{ [(x \div 2) - 4 + 5] \times 3 \} \div 2) + 7 = x$$

I solved it by guessing numbers until I found one that worked, but you could use algebra to save time:

$$(\{ [\tfrac{x}{2} + 1] \times 3 \} \div 2) + 7 = x$$
$$(\{ \tfrac{3x}{2} + 3 \} \div 2) + 7 = x$$
$$(\tfrac{3x}{4} + 1.5) + 7 = x$$
$$\tfrac{3x}{4} + 8.5 = x$$
$$8.5 = \tfrac{x}{4}$$
$$8.5 \times 4 = x = 34$$

[4] After Shadow came

We had two cats, and then four kittens, so now we have a total of six cats. Two-thirds of them are girl cats, which means we have four girl cats. One of them is the mother, Shadow, so the other three are girl kittens.

[5] I SPENT $8

We work backward: $4 left + the $8 spent = $12 in the beginning.

[6] KELLY'S FAMILY HAD DOGS

In the end, all the original dogs came home, plus Kelly had collected an equal number of stuffed dogs: five real dogs + five stuffed animals = ten dogs in all.

[7] MRS. STERNS HAS TWO RECIPES

Mrs. Sterns needs 63 + 52 = 115 oz. Therefore, she must buy 120 oz., which will be 120 ÷ 20 = 6 bags.

[8] I AM AN ODD NUMBER

The odd square numbers less than fifty are 1, 9, 25, and 49. Of these, only nine is divisible by three.

[9] I DO A PIROUETTE TURN

Solution: 1 × 4 counts + 32 × 2 counts = 68 counts in all.

[10] YOU MAKE ABOUT $27

"About" means we will round off the numbers as we calculate. You spent 75 × $.25 = $18.75 to buy the cans, which is about $19 (rounding up the cents), and your profit was about $27. Therefore, you earned about $19 + 27 = $46 from sale of forty-six cans. You must have sold them for about $1 each.

[11] WE WENT TO CANADA

Solution: 4 liters ÷ 3 = 1 ⅓ liter = about 1.33 liter per small bag.

[12] AT THE BLACK GATE

If one-third of the orcs were killed, that means two-thirds of them lived through dinner. Then if two-fifths of those were killed, we know that three-fifths survived to join the morning's battle:

$$\text{⅗ of ⅔ of the original 450 orcs}$$
$$= \text{⅗} \times \text{⅔} \times 450$$
$$= 180 \text{ orcs who survived.}$$

[13] THE NEW FAMILY

The key to this puzzle is realizing that no one is a sibling to him- or herself. When the boy said he had twice as many sisters as brothers, he was not counting himself among the brothers. And the girl didn't count herself.

I made up a sort of family algebra, a shorthand way to remember each child's statement. Let b stand for the total number of boys (and g for the girls) in the new family. Then the new boy has $b - 1$ brothers, one less than the number of boys in the family, while he has g sisters. And if he has twice as many sisters as brothers, then $g = 2 (b - 1)$.

But the girl has the same number of brothers and sisters. Since she has b brothers and $g - 1$ sisters, that means $b = g - 1$, so there must be fewer boys than girls in the

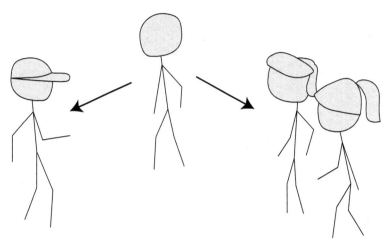

The boy doesn't see himself, so he counts
one brother and two sisters.

new family. My sketch of four children will fit the boy's statement, but not his sister's.

I can just try numbers until I find the right combination, or I could use algebraic substitution to solve these equations:

$$g = 2 \, (b - 1)$$
$$\text{and}$$
$$b = g - 1$$
$$\text{so}$$
$$g = 2 \, (\, [g - 1] - 1)$$
$$g = 2 \, (g - 2)$$
$$g = 2g - 4$$
$$g = 4$$
$$b = 3$$

The new family has seven children in all: four girls and three boys.

[14] A'HMOSE'S SECRET NUMBER PUZZLE

Let's call the number your friend picks "N." After he adds two-thirds more, he has:

$$N + \tfrac{2}{3} \times N = \tfrac{5}{3} \times N$$

Then he takes away one-third of that. Remember that "of" means to multiply the fractions, which gives:

$$\tfrac{5}{3} \times N - (\tfrac{1}{3} \times \tfrac{5}{3}) \, N$$
$$= \tfrac{5}{3} \times N - \tfrac{5}{9} \times N$$
$$= \tfrac{15}{9} \times N - \tfrac{5}{9} \times N$$
$$= \tfrac{10}{9} \times N$$

Finally, you subtract one-tenth of this answer:

$$\tfrac{10}{9} \times N - (\tfrac{1}{10} \times \tfrac{10}{9}) \, N$$

$$= \tfrac{10}{9} \times N - \tfrac{1}{9} \times N$$
$$= \tfrac{9}{9} \times N = N$$

Therefore, we end up with the original number. The trick will always work, no matter what number we choose.

[15] How many soldiers

One way to solve problems like this is to work out the clues on a hundred chart. Let's start with the rows of five soldiers, which leave three extra men. That means the possible number of soldiers is three more than a multiple of five, so circle all the numbers on the hundred chart that end in three or eight.

In rows of six, there are five men left out, which means we are one man short of filling the next row. So we need to find numbers that are one less than a multiple of six. On your hundred chart, cross out six and all its multiples, and then look for numbers that come just before one of these marks. Check your circled numbers, and cross out all that don't work.

For instance, $3 \times 6 = 18$ and $18 - 1 = 17$, but that doesn't match our first clue. But $4 \times 6 = 24$ and $24 - 1 = 23$, and that matches a circled number. Twenty-three is the smallest number that works with both of the conditions we checked so far. Can you find two more numbers?

Finally, check the last condition: two more than a multiple of three. It so happens that in this case, all of our remaining numbers fit the condition. If a number is five more than a multiple of six, then it will automatically be two more than a multiple of three.

So the number of soldiers could be twenty-three (smallest possible answer) or fifty-three, or eighty-three. And if we continue the pattern, it could be any number of the form $23 + 30n$, where n can be any whole number.

Remainder problems of this sort always have more than one possible answer.

[16] The emperor and the tortoise

The dots are the numbers in a three by three magic square. That means the numbers in each row, column, and diagonal add up to the same sum. In this case, the sum is fifteen. Black dots are even numbers, and white dots are odd. Here is the magic square:

4	9	2
3	5	7
8	1	6

[The following method is described by Sir Thomas Little Heath in *A History of Greek Mathematics, Volume 1.*[†] Others have speculated about different methods that Thales might have used.]

"If triangles have two angles and one side equal,
then the triangles are congruent."

The trick is to make two congruent triangles: one going out to the ship, and the other staying on shore, where distance can be measured. As Thales stands at his vantage point, he holds the tall rod vertical (with the help of a plumb line) so that the height of the tower or cliff plus the tall part of the rod makes one side of the triangle, which will be the same length for both triangles.

The angle at the base of the tower or cliff will remain the same, so the next thing Thales needs to do is find the other angle, the angle at the top of his rod. He looks along the smaller stick and adjusts it until he can see it pointing at the far-away ship. Finally, keeping the angle of the hinge the same, he turns the rod to sight along the shoreline. Whatever the rod then points at will be the same distance away as the ship at sea.

One triangle is from Thales to the ship. The other triangle is from Thales along the shore. They are congruent, because the height (rod + tower/cliff) and its two angles stay the same. And because the triangles are congruent, all the corresponding sides are equal. Most distances near Miletus are probably well known, but if Thales is measuring along an unfamiliar shoreline, he can tell his helper a landmark to which he should run. The helper counts his steps to find the distance.

Actually, the runner would count every other step (for instance, every time his left foot hit the ground). The Greek unit *bēma* was a double pace, equal to about 1.5 meter.

BHĀSKARA'S BEAUTIFUL BOOK

[18] We have $\frac{1}{3} + \frac{1}{5} + \frac{1}{6} + \frac{1}{4}$ of the water lilies given away, and then six remain that we can give to the teacher. What is the total fraction of water lilies given?

$$\frac{1}{3} + \frac{1}{5} + \frac{1}{6} + \frac{1}{4} = ?$$

Find a common denominator: $5 \times 6 = 30$, and three will also go into thirty, but four will not. If, however, we double thirty, we find that four will go into sixty, so we can use that as our common denominator:

$$\frac{20}{60} + \frac{12}{60} + \frac{10}{60} + \frac{15}{60} = \frac{57}{60}$$

So the remaining six lilies are three-sixtieths of the whole set:

$$6 = \frac{3}{60} \times N = \frac{1}{20} \times N$$
$$N = 20 \times 6 = 120 \text{ water lilies.}$$

[19] The traveler spent half of his money at Pryag, leaving a remainder of half the money. He spent two-ninths of the remainder at Benares, leaving him seven-ninths of half the money:

$$\frac{7}{9} \times \frac{1}{2} = \frac{7}{18}$$

[†] *http://books.google.com/books?id=h4JsAAAAMAAJ*

So he had seven-eighteenths of the money he started with. Then he had to pay customs and other expenses, which took one-fourth of that money, leaving him three-fourths of the seven-eighteenths:

$$\tfrac{3}{4} \times \tfrac{7}{18} = \tfrac{7}{24}$$

At that point, he was down to seven twenty-fourths of his original amount. Last, he spent six-tenths of that at Gaya, which left him with four-tenths of the seven twenty-fourths:

$$\tfrac{4}{10} \times \tfrac{7}{24} = \tfrac{7}{60}$$

And the story tells us that this last amount, seven-sixtieths of what he started with, was sixty-three of whatever type of coin they used. We can call it dollars, and now we can figure:

$$\tfrac{7}{60} \text{ of the money} = \$63$$
$$\tfrac{1}{60} \text{ of the money} = \$63 \div 7 = \$9$$
$$60 \times \$9 = \$540$$

So the traveler started with $540, or 540 of whatever currency the Hindus of that time were using.

[20] Once again, we need to figure out what fraction of the bees have flown away. The remainder will be our one lonely bee who cannot make up his mind which flower to visit. But the trickiest part is that we are not given a direct fraction for the bees that flew to the arbour:

$$\tfrac{1}{5} + \tfrac{1}{3} + [3 \times (\tfrac{1}{3} - \tfrac{1}{5})] = \text{flown bees}$$

Choose $3 \times 5 = 15$ as the common denominator:

$$\tfrac{3}{15} + \tfrac{5}{15} + [3 \times (\tfrac{5}{15} - \tfrac{3}{15})] = ?$$
$$\tfrac{8}{15} + [3 \times \tfrac{2}{15}] = ?$$
$$\tfrac{8}{15} + \tfrac{6}{15} = \tfrac{14}{15}$$

So our lonely bee is one-fifteenth of the whole hive, which means there must have been fifteen bees at the beginning.

[21] Bhāskara's dissection:

This diagram proves the Pythagorean Theorem.

The first, large square is the square of the hypotenuse—that is, it's a square with sides the length of the triangle's hypotenuse. The square is cut apart into four equal right triangles plus a small square with its side equal to the difference between the sides of the triangle.

In the second drawing, the pieces are rearranged to create two squares with sides the length of the triangle's two sides. Imagine a line drawn as shown, which will help

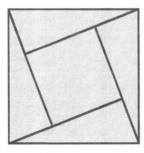
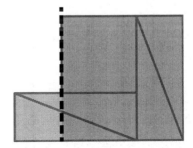

you see the squares. Therefore, the square on the hypotenuse is the same size (covers the same total area) as the sum of the squares on the other two sides. This is true no matter what size right triangles you draw.

AL-KHWĀRIZMĪ'S ALGEBRA

[22] In each of these problems, the two parts will be x and $10 - x$. In this problem, the parts were divided, so:

$$(10 - x) \div x = 4$$
$$10 - x = 4x$$
$$2 = x$$

The parts are two and eight.

Your student could have started with the following equation and solved the problem just as well:

$$x \div (10 - x) = 4$$
$$x = 4 \times (10 - x)$$
$$x = 40 - 4x$$
$$5x = 40$$
$$x = 8$$

Again, the parts are eight and two.

[23] The two parts are x and $10 - x$, so:

$$(10 - x) \times x = 21$$
$$10x - x^2 = 21$$

Al-Khwārizmī would have converted this to the problem "a square and twenty-one dirhems are equal to ten roots" and then solved it by a convoluted series of geometric constructions. Instead, we'll use simple factoring:

$$x^2 - 10x + 21 = 0$$
$$(x - 3)(x - 7) = 0$$

The parts are three and seven.

[24] The two parts are x and $10 - x$. To multiply a part by itself means to square it, so:

$$(10 - x)^2 = 81x$$
$$100 - 20x + x^2 = 81x$$
$$x^2 - 101x + 100 = 0$$
$$(x - 1)(x - 100) = 0$$

Either $x = 1$ or $x = 100$ will solve the equation, but only $x = 1$ fits the conditions of the problem. The parts are one and nine.

Your student could have started with the following equation and solved the problem just as well:

$$x^2 = 81(10 - x)$$

In this case, you would have found the answers $x = 9$ or $x = -90$. Again, only one of these fits the conditions of the problem.

[25] The two parts are x and $10 - x$. To multiply a part by itself means to square it, so:

$$x^2 + (10 - x)^2 = 58$$

$$x^2 + (100 - 20x + x^2) = 58$$
$$x^2 + 100 - 20x + x^2 = 58$$
$$2x^2 - 20x + 100 = 58$$
$$x^2 - 10x + 50 = 29$$
$$x^2 - 10x + 21 = 0$$
$$(x - 3)(x - 7) = 0$$

The parts are three and seven.

[26] The two parts are x and $10 - x$. This one is tricky with fractions:

$$\frac{x}{(10-x)} + \frac{(10-x)}{x} = 2 + \tfrac{1}{6}$$
$$\frac{x}{(10-x)} + \frac{(10-x)}{x} = 1\tfrac{5}{6}$$

To clear the fractions, multiply through by all the denominators.

$$6x^2 + 6 \times (10 - x)^2 = 13 \times (10 - x) \times x$$
$$6x^2 + 6 \times (100 - 20x + x^2) = (130 - 13x) \times x$$
$$6x^2 + 600 - 120x + 6x^2 = 130x - 13x^2$$
$$25x^2 - 250x + 600 = 0$$
$$x^2 - 10x + 24 = 0$$
$$(x - 4)(x - 6) = 0$$

The parts are four and six.

FIBONACCI'S STORY PROBLEMS

[27] Add up the numbers of each item:

7 old men
(7×7) mules = 49
$(7 \times 7 \times 7)$ sacks = 343
$(7 \times 7 \times 7 \times 7)$ loaves = 2401
$(7 \times 7 \times 7 \times 7 \times 7)$ knives = 16,807
$(7 \times 7 \times 7 \times 7 \times 7 \times 7)$ sheaths = 117,649
= 137,256 in all.

[28] Work backward, starting with the man's final apple and adding back in however many he must have given each guard. For example, he gave the last guard "half his apples and one apple more" and was left with one apple. So before he gave the "one more" he must have had two apples, and that means he must have had twice two (that is, four) apples before he gave the last guard any of them:

The man had one apple when he left the seventh guard.
Before he gave "one more" = 2 apples.
Before he gave "half his apples" = 4 apples.

He had four apples when he left the sixth guard.
Before "one more" = 5 apples.
Before "half his apples" = 10 apples.

He had ten apples when he left the fifth guard.
Before "one more" = 11 apples.
Before "half his apples" = 22 apples.

He had twenty-two apples when he left the fourth guard.
    Before "one more" = 23 apples.
    Before "half his apples" = 46 apples.

He had forty-six apples when he left the third guard.
    Before "one more" = 47 apples.
    Before "half his apples" = 94 apples.

He had ninety-four apples when he left the second guard.
    Before "one more" = 95 apples.
    Before "half his apples" = 190 apples.

He had 190 apples when he left the first guard.
    Before "one more" = 191 apples.
    Before "half his apples" = 382 apples.
    The man gathered 382 apples.

[29] Count the rabbits in pairs:

January = one pair of babies.

February = one pair still, now half-grown.

March = one pair of adults produces one pair of babies = two pairs in all.

April = one pair of adults produces one pair of babies, and last month's babies are now half-grown = three pairs.

May = two pairs of adults produce two pairs of babies, and last month's babies are now half-grown = five pairs.

June = three pairs of adults produce three pairs of babies, and last month's babies are now half-grown = eight pairs.

July = thirteen pairs.

August = twenty-one pairs.

September = thirty-four pairs.

October = fifty-five pairs.

November = eighty-nine pairs.

And December = 144 pairs = 288 rabbits in all.

This problem is the source of the famous Fibonacci Series: 1, 1, 2, 3, 5, 8, 13, etc., where each number is the sum of the two previous numbers. The Fibonacci Series can be interesting to study because it shows up in so many different places. For instance, the number of petals on a flower is often a Fibonacci number.

[30] NAPIER'S CHESSBOARD CALCULATOR

To add numbers, first set them out in tokens on the chessboard. Use one row for each number. When you are sure the numbers are set up right, it's time to combine the rows. Now you need to double up until there is no more than one token in any column. To double up, start on the right: if you have two tokens in the ones column, that is the same as one token in the twos. Two tokens in the twos column is the same as one in the fours. Two fours make one eight, etc.

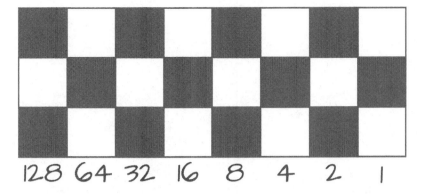

128 64 32 16 8 4 2 1

To subtract numbers, set out your original amount in one of the higher rows. Arrange the number you want to subtract below it. Check that your tokens are set up right. Now remove from your original number one token to match each of the tokens in the number you are subtracting.

If you have an empty column in your original number, you may need to double down. For instance, if you have a token in the fours column but none in the twos, and you need to take away a two, then double down the four: one token in the fours column is worth two in the twos. Then you will be able to take away one of the twos.

Finally, convert your answer back to a normal, base ten number. For every token in your answer, add what that column is worth. So 1101 would mean 8 + 4 + 1 = 13.

For a complete explanation of Napier's calculator, read *Knotted Doughnuts and other Mathematical Entertainments* by Martin Gardner.

[31] BERTRAND RUSSELL'S BARBER

As the story stands, the barber cannot exist. A man who shaves himself because he doesn't shave himself is pure nonsense.

Someone might try to fix up mathematical logic by saying that, like the barber, certain types of sets are pure nonsense. For instance, perhaps sets that are defined with the word "all" (as in, "all sets which are not members of themselves") cannot really exist. Therefore, the supposed contradiction vanishes.

Another solution would be if the barber did not himself live in the town. Then he could shave himself whenever he pleased with no contradictions. Similarly, someone might say no set can be considered a member of itself. Then, of course, the contradiction vanishes.

Neither of these solutions sounds "right" to our intuitive understanding of sets. Nor were the axioms by which Zermelo rescued mathematical logic completely satisfying, but mathematical beggars could not afford to be choosy.

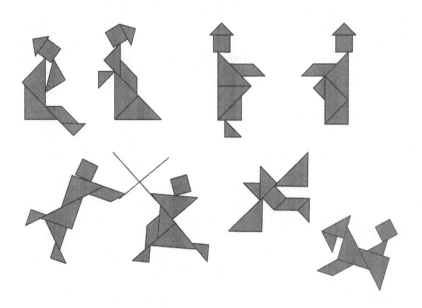

Appendix D

Quotes and Reference Links

I LOVE QUOTATIONS. EVERYTHING I could ever want to say has probably been said by someone else (who probably did not think of it first, either). At least a few of those people had a wonderful way with words.

Some of the quotations in this book are from my own reading. Others are gleaned from two websites that I visit often to browse: Furman University's Mathematical Quotation Server and the Mathematical and Educational Quotation Server at Westfield State College.

http://math.furman.edu/~mwoodard/mquot.html
http://www.wsc.mass.edu/math/faculty/fleron/quotes

AL-KHWĀRIZMĪ, MUHAMMAD IBN MŪSÁ. *The Algebra of Muhammad ben Musa,* edited and translated by Frederic Rosen, Oriental Translation Fund, 1831; available at Google Books.
http://books.google.com/books?id=3bNDAAAAIAAJ

ANDERSON, DOUGLAS R. "Taxicab Geometry Worksheet," Math 105, Spring 2010, Concordia College Moorhead website.
http://www.cord.edu/faculty/andersod/TaxicabWorksheets.pdf

BALL, DEBORAH LOEWENBERG. "Magical Hopes: Manipulatives and the Reform of Math Education," *American Educator,* vol. 16 (1992), no. 2, 14–18 and 46–47.

BEECHICK, RUTH. "If you stay with meaningful mental arithmetic ..." from *An Easy Start in Arithmetic (Grades K–3),* Arrow Press, 1986.

—. "I'll let you in on a secret ..." from *You Can Teach Your Child Successfully,* Arrow Press, 1988.

BELL, E. T. "Compared to what glorious Greece ..."from *Men of Mathematics,* Simon and Schuster, 1937.

BENEZET, LOUIS P. "The Teaching of Arithmetic: The Story of an Experiment," originally published in the *Journal of the National Education Association,* vol. 24–25 (1935–1936); available at the Benezet Centre website.
http://www.inference.phy.cam.ac.uk/sanjoy/benezet/three.html

BHĀSKARA ĀCHĀRYA. *Lilawati: or, A treatise on arithmetic and geometry,* translated by John Taylor, Courier Press, 1816; available at Google Books.
http://books.google.com/books?id=0KMIAAAAQAAJ

BLANKE, BARBARA. *Using the Rekenrek as a Visual Model for Strategic Reasoning in*

Mathematics, The Math Learning Center, 2008.
http://bridges1.mathlearningcenter.org/media/Rekenrek_0308.pdf

BOALER, JO. "There is a huge elephant ..." from "Unlocking Children's Math Potential: 5 Research Results to Transform Math Learning," academic paper, YouCubed
website, 2015. Boaler is a Stanford University Professor of Mathematics Education and the co-founder of YouCubed.org, which hosts a variety of resources to
encourage students and parents who struggle with math.
https://www.youcubed.org/wp-content/uploads/2015/03/teacher-article-youcubed2.pdf
https://www.youcubed.org

BRENNAN, JULIE. "Early exposure to real mathematics ..." from the introduction to the
Living Math website. Brennan is a veteran home educator, founder of the Living
Math Forum, and the author of the *Living Math Through History* lesson plans.
http://www.livingmath.net
https://groups.yahoo.com/neo/groups/LivingMathForum/info

CARDONE, TINA. *Nix the Tricks: A guide to avoiding shortcuts that cut out math concept
development,* self-published, 2013.
http://nixthetricks.com

CARROLL, LEWIS. "Can you do addition ..." from *Through the Looking Glass, and What
Alice Found There,* (Macmillan, 1872); available at Internet Archive. Carroll was
the pen name of mathematician Charles Lutwidge Dodgson, who published several books of mathematical puzzles and games, which he felt were valuable as
teaching aids, as well as writing serious mathematical papers and textbooks.
https://archive.org/details/throughlooking00carr

CARSON, RACHEL. "If a child is to keep ..." from *The Sense of Wonder,* Harper & Row,
1965.

DANCIS, JEROME. "What must we add to 4 to obtain 9 as the sum?" from "Reading
Instruction for Arithmetic Word Problems: If Johnny can't read and follow direc-
tions, then he can't do math," an expansion of his article "When It Comes To
Math, Words Count", *Washington Post,* September 8, 2002, B04; University of
Maryland website, July 17, 2007.
http://www2.math.umd.edu/~jnd/subhome/Reading_Instruction.htm

—. "Supposedly Difficult Arithmetic Word Problems: Keep It Simple for Students,"
University of Maryland website, January 2003.
http://www2.math.umd.edu/~jnd/Difficult_Word_Problems.html

DANIELSON, CHRISTOPHER. "I have spent the last four days ..." from "Let the children play," Talking Math with Your Kids blog, August 31, 2015. With his blogs
and other projects, Danielson helps parents and teachers understand how children
understand math.
http://talkingmathwithkids.com/2015/08/31/let-the-children-play
http://talkingmathwithkids.com/mathonastick
https://christopherdanielson.wordpress.com

—. "If you can read with your kids ..." from *Talking Math with Your Kids,* self-pub-

lished, 2013.
http://talkingmathwithkids.com

—. *Common Core Math for Parents for Dummies,* John Wiley & Sons, 2015. Check out the video resource center with bonus material explaining the concepts and techniques.
http://www.dummies.com/Section/id-824962.html

DEVLIN, KEITH. "Mathematical thinking is more than …" from "What is mathematical thinking?" Devlin's Angle blog, September 1, 2012. Devlin is a mathematician at Stanford University and the author of many books and several blogs.
http://devlinsangle.blogspot.com/2012/08/what-is-mathematical-thinking.html

—. *Mathematics: The Science of Patterns: The Search for Order in Life, Mind and the Universe,* Macmillan, 1996.

—. "It Ain't No Repeated Addition," Devlin's Angle, June 2008.
https://www.maa.org/external_archive/devlin/devlin_06_08.html

—. "It's Still Not Repeated Addition," Devlin's Angle, July-August 2008.
https://www.maa.org/external_archive/devlin/devlin_0708_08.html

—. "Multiplication and Those Pesky British Spellings," Devlin's Angle, September 2008.
https://www.maa.org/external_archive/devlin/devlin_09_08.html

—. "What Exactly is Multiplication?" Devlin's Angle, January 2011.
https://www.maa.org/external_archive/devlin/devlin_01_11.html

DIRAC, PAUL. "The mathematician plays …" from a lecture delivered on the presentation of the James Scott prize, February 6, 1939. Published in *Proceedings of the Royal Society (Edinburgh),* Vol. 59, 1938-39.
http://www.damtp.cam.ac.uk/events/strings02/dirac/speach.html

DODD, SANDRA. "Unschoolers and Mathematics," Sandra Dodd website.
http://sandradodd.com/math

DROUJKOVA, MARIA. "When a kid is feeling bad …" from a Natural Math Forum discussion of math club activities, February 3, 2011. Droujkova founded Natural Math, an online community to share beautiful, playful, and intuitive mathematics. She is a co-author of *Moebius Noodles: Adventurous Math for the Playground Crowd.*
https://groups.google.com/d/msg/naturalmath/yW5Pdr8_WhI/h9xULrj1-4wJ
http://naturalmath.com

EINSTEIN, ALBERT. "It is in fact nothing short …" quoted by H. Eves in *Return to Mathematical Circles,* PWS-Kent Pub. Co., 1988.

—. "Learning is experience …" quoted hundreds of times in books and on websites, but I can't find any reference that credits the original source. Although Einstein may not have said it himself, the quote clearly resonates with many people's experience of learning.

ERDŐS, PAUL. "Why are numbers beautiful? …" quoted by Keith Devlin in *The Math Gene: How Mathematical Thinking Evolved And Why Numbers Are Like Gossip,* Basic Books, 2000.

EVES, HOWARD. "It is impossible to overstate …" and "There is a distinction …" quoted by Rosemary Schmalz in *Out of the Mouths of Mathematicians: A Quotation Book for Philomaths*, Mathematical Association of America, 1993.

FINKEL, DAN. "I've spent the last two …" from "Good Mistakes, Constant Mistakes," Math for Love blog, February 28, 2009. Dan runs workshops on mathematics education and is a regular contributor to the *New York Times* Numberplay blog. *http://mathforlove.com/2009/02/82223587*

FLANDERS, J. R. "How much of the content in mathematics textbooks is new?" (1987), *Arithmetic Teacher*, vol. 35 (1987), no. 1, 18–23.

FURUTA, BURT. "The root problem …" from "Guest Post: Understanding is Misunderstood," Math Mama Writes blog, June 12, 2013. *http://mathmamawrites.blogspot.com/2013/06/guest-post-understanding-is.html*

GARDNER, MARTIN. "Biographical history, as taught …" quoted by George F. Simmons in *Calculus Gems: Brief Lives and Memorable Mathematics*, McGraw-Hill, 1992. Gardner may be best known for his long-standing "Mathematical Games" column in *Scientific American*, but he also wrote more than two dozen challenging books of puzzles and brainteasers.

—. "The best way …" from *Mathematical Carnival: From Penny Puzzles, Card Shuffles and Tricks of Lightning Calculators to Roller Coaster Rides into the Fourth Dimension*, Random House, 1975.

—. "With a little guidance …" in the foreword to *Mathematics: A Human Endeavor* by Harold R. Jacobs, W. H. Freeman, 1982.

GARLIKOV, RICK. "Most adults, including teachers …" from "'Explaining' Math Poorly," Garlikov website. Garlikov teaches philosophy at Troy University and has written many online articles on philosophy and education. *http://www.garlikov.com/teaching/badexplan.htm* *http://www.garlikov.com/schools.htm*

GASKINS, DENISE. "Subtracting Mixed Numbers: A Cry for Help," Let's Play Math blog, March 26, 2008. *http://denisegaskins.com/2008/03/26/subtracting-mixed-numbers-a-cry-for-help*

—. "If It Ain't Repeated Addition, What Is It?" Let's Play Math, July 1, 2008. *http://denisegaskins.com/2008/07/01/if-it-aint-repeated-addition*

—. "What's Wrong with 'Repeated Addition'?" Let's Play Math, July 28, 2008. *http://denisegaskins.com/2008/07/28/whats-wrong-with-repeated-addition*

—. "Word Problems from Literature," Let's Play Math blog, April 26, 2010. *http://denisegaskins.com/2010/04/26/word-problems-from-literature*

—. "PUFM 1.5 Multiplication, Part 1," Let's Play Math blog, July 16, 2012. *http://denisegaskins.com/2012/07/16/pufm-1-5-multiplication-part-1*

—. "Infinite Cake: Don Cohen's Infinite Series for Kids," Let's Play Math, July 2, 2015. *http://denisegaskins.com/2015/07/02/infinite-cake-don-cohens-infinite-series-for-kids*

—. "Posts Tagged 'Math Games'," Let's Play Math blog, assorted dates. *http://denisegaskins.com/category/all-about-math/activities/games*

GLAISHER, J. W. L. "I am sure that no subject ..." quoted by Florian Cajori in *A History Of Mathematics*, Macmillan & Company, 1893; available at Google Books.
http://books.google.com/books?id=bfgRxVzjbMYC

GLEIZER, OLEG. "Math is freedom ..." in a recorded discussion on the Math 2.0 site, October 20, 2011. Gleizer's Creative Commons (CC BY-NC-SA 3.0) book *Modern Math for Elementary Schoolers* is available free for download.
http://mathfuture.wikispaces.com/ModernMathOlegGleizer
http://www.naturalmath.com/DeltaStreamMedia/OlegGleizerModernMathematics _12_2011.pdf

GOLDEN, JOHN. "The toughest thing ..." from "Elementary Homeschool," Math Hombre blog, August 2, 2010. Golden's blog includes a variety of games and plenty of sound educational philosophy, and it's well worth browsing.
http://mathhombre.blogspot.com/2010/08/elementary-homeschool.html
http://mathhombre.blogspot.com/p/games.html

—. "Instrumental vs. Relational," Math Hombre blog, February 15, 2011.
http://mathhombre.blogspot.com/2011/02/instrumental-vs-relational.html

GREENBERG, DANIEL. "And 'Rithmetic" from *Free at Last: The Sudbury Valley School,* Sudbury Valley School Press, 1995; available at Scribd.
http://www.scribd.com/doc/14389275/And-Rithmetic-by-Daniel-Greenberg#scribd

GROSS, HERB. "As important as mathematics is ..." quoted by Jerome Dancis in "Reading Instruction for Arithmetic Word Problems," July 17, 2007. Gross has over 50 years of teaching experience in diverse settings ranging from Central Prison's Death Row in Raleigh, NC, to MIT's Center for Advanced Engineering Study.
http://www2.math.umd.edu/~jnd/subhome/Reading_Instruction.htm

—. "If we gained weight ..." from "Calculus in Everyday Life," Math as a Second Language website.
http://adjectivenounmath.com/sitebuildercontent/sitebuilderfiles/calculus_in_everyday_life1.pdf

—. "What's really neat ..." from the Mathematics as a Second Language website.
http://adjectivenounmath.com/index.html

GU, WENYUAN. "Were Our Mathematics Textbooks a Mile Wide and an Inch Deep?" academic paper, September 2010, ERIC Archive.
http://files.eric.ed.gov/fulltext/ED511928.pdf

HALMOS, PAUL. "Study actively ..." from *I want to be a Mathematician: An Automathography,* Springer, 1985.

HANKEL, HERMANN. "In most sciences ..." quoted by Stanley Gudder in *A Mathematical Journey*, McGraw-Hill, 1994.

HARDY, G. H. "A mathematician, like a painter ..." from *A Mathematician's Apology*, Cambridge University Press, 1940.

HEATH, SIR THOMAS LITTLE. *A History of Greek Mathematics, Volume 1,* Clarendon Press, 1921, available at Google books.
http://books.google.com/books?id=h4JsAAAAMAAJ

HOPE, JACK, ET AL. *Mental Math in the Primary Grades; Mental Math in the Middle Grades;* and *Mental Math in Junior High,* Dale Seymour Publications, 1987–1990. These books appear to be out of print, so try your library or a used book website.

JACKSON, BILL. "There are 21 girls in a class. There are 3 times as many girls as boys …" from "The Singapore Math Model-Drawing Approach," The Daily Riff, November 9, 2010.
http://www.thedailyriff.com/2010/11/singapore-math-demystified-part-3-the-famous-bar-models.php

KASNER, EDWARD. "Puzzles in one sense …" from *Mathematics and the Imagination,* Simon and Schuster, 1940.

KOVALEVSKAYA, SOFIA. "Many who have never had …" quoted by W. Dunham in *The Mathematical Universe: An Alphabetical Journey Through the Great Proofs, Problems, and Personalities,* John Wiley & Sons, 1994.

KOZOL, JONATHAN. "If you could lead …" quoted in the Mathematical and Educational Quotation Server.
http://www.westfield.ma.edu/math/faculty/fleron/quotes/viewquote.asp?letter=k

KUPPE, MARTIN. "Mathematistan: The Landscape of Mathematics," from "Mathematics: Measuring × laziness^2 (Earthlings 101, Episode 13)" by Zogg from Betelgeuse, YouTube, June 30, 2014.
https://youtu.be/XqpvBaiJRHo

LOCKHART, PAUL. "There is no ulterior …" from "A Mathematician's Lament," academic paper, 2002; available at the Mathematical Association of America website. An expanded version was released as a paperback: *A Mathematician's Lament: How School Cheats Us Out of Our Most Fascinating and Imaginative Art Form,* Bellevue Literary Press, 2009. Lockhart teaches math at St. Ann's School in Brooklyn, New York.
http://www.maa.org/external_archive/devlin/LockhartsLament.pdf

—. "I would have expected …" from the video trailer for his book *Measurement,* Harvard University Press, 2012.
https://youtu.be/V1gT2f3Fe44

MASON, CHARLOTTE. "I know you may bring a horse …" combined excerpts from "Schoolbooks and How They Make for Education," *The Parents' Review,* volume 11 (1900), 448–464; and *Towards a Philosophy of Education,* 1923; available at Ambleside Online.
http://amblesideonline.org/PR/PR11p448Schoolbooks.shtml
http://www.amblesideonline.org/CM/toc.html#6

McMANAMAN, YELENA. "Our own experience …" from "Math Goggles Challenges," Moebius Noodles blog, January 21, 2013. McManaman is a co-author of *Moebius Noodles: Adventurous Math for the Playground Crowd.*
http://www.moebiusnoodles.com/math-goggles-challenges

NGUYEN, FAWN. "I'm not worried about …" from the "Teachers" page at her Math Talks site. Nguyen teaches math at Mesa Union Junior High, blogs about her students' learning, and moderates the fantastic Visual Patterns website.

http://www.mathtalks.net/teachers.html
http://fawnnguyen.com
http://www.visualpatterns.org

PADRON, ROBIN. "If we have never ..." and "Story time is precious ..." from *How to Homeschool Math—Even if you Hate Fractions!!* Self-published, 2011. Robin teaches math in Connecticut and does private math tutoring for public- and private-school students, as well as for homeschoolers.

PAULOS, JOHN ALLEN. "If mathematics education ..." from *Innumeracy: Mathematical Illiteracy and Its Consequences,* Macmillan, 2011.

PESEK, DOLORES D. and David Kirshner. "Interference of Instrumental Instruction in Subsequent Relational Learning," *Journal for Research in Mathematics Education,* vol. 31 (2000), no. 5, 524–540.

http://academic.sun.ac.za/mathed/174/relinstrumental.pdf

PÉTER, RÓZSA. "I love mathematics ..." quoted by Rosemary Schmalz in *Out of the Mouths of Mathematicians: A Quotation Book for Philomaths,* Mathematical Association of America, 1993.

POINCARÉ, JULES HENRI. "The mathematician does not ..." quoted by H.E.Huntley in *The Divine Proportion: A Study in Mathematical Beauty,* Dover Publications, 1970.

POLIKOFF, MORGAN S. "The Redundancy of Mathematics Instruction in U.S. Elementary and Middle Schools," *The Elementary School Journal,* vol. 113 (2012), no. 2, 230–251.

http://web-app.usc.edu/web/rossier/publications/66/The%20Redundancy%20of%20 Math%20Instruction.pdf

POLYA, GEORGE. "A great discovery ..." and "A teacher of mathematics ..." and "Solving problems..." from *How to Solve It: A New Aspect of Mathematical Method,* Princeton University Press, 1957.

ROTHSTEIN, EDWARD. "Real mathematics is not ..." from "Making Math Magical," *Family Life,* September/October 1996.

RUSSELL, BERTRAND. "It seemed to me ..." from *My Philosophical Development,* Allen and Unwin, 1959.

—. "Mathematics, rightly viewed ..." from "The Study of Mathematics," *Mysticism and Logic: And Other Essays,* Longmans, Green and Company, 1919; available at Google Books.

http://books.google.com/books?id=zwMQAAAAYAAJ

SAWYER, W. W. "The best way to learn ..." and "Everyone knows that it is easy ..." from *Mathematician's Delight,* Penguin Books, 1943; available at Internet Archive. Sawyer was a British mathematician and educator whose life spanned most of the twentieth century.

https://archive.org/details/MathematiciansDelight
http://wwsawyer.org/default.html

—. "A widespread fallacy ..." and "It is not enough for a child to hear ..." and "Most remarks made by children …" from *Vision in Elementary Mathematics*, Penguin Books, 1964.

SENGER, NICK. "Paraphrasing is one of …" from "Quotes about Reading for Students to Ponder and Paraphrase," Teen Literacy Tips blog, September 12, 2007.
http://www.nicksenger.com/blog/quotes-about-reading-for-students-to-ponder-and-paraphrase

SKEMP, RICHARD. "Suppose that a teacher reminds a class …" from "Relational Understanding and Instrumental Understanding," *Mathematics Teaching*, 77 (1976), 20–26.
http://www.grahamtall.co.uk/skemp/pdfs/instrumental-relational.pdf
http://www.skemp.org.uk/

STEEN, LYNN ARTHUR. "As biology is the science of life …" from "Reflections on Mathematical Patterns, Relationships, and Functions," academic paper prepared for the Minnesota K–12 Mathematics Framework, SciMath-MN, Minnesota Department of Children, Families, and Learning, 1998. See also "The Science of Patterns," *Science*, vol. 240, no. 4852, April 29, 1988.
http://www.stolaf.edu/people/steen/Papers/98algebra_mn.pdf
http://www.stolaf.edu/people/steen/Papers/88sci_patterns.pdf

STIGLER, JAMES W. and James Hiebert. *The Teaching Gap: Best Ideas from the World's Teachers for Improving Education in the Classroom*, Simon and Schuster, 2009.

STROGATZ, STEVEN. "The Elements of Math," *The New York Times*, January–May 2010.
http://topics.nytimes.com/top/opinion/series/steven_strogatz_on_the_elements_of_math/index.html

—. *The Joy of x: A Guided Tour of Math, from One to Infinity*, Eamon Dolan/Houghton Mifflin Harcourt, 2012.

TANTON, JAMES. "The high-school English curriculum …" from "Goal of this Site," Thinking Mathematics website. Tanton worked as a college professor for a decade, as a high-school teacher for a decade, and is now the Mathematician in Residence at the Mathematical Association of America in Washington D.C.
http://www.jamestanton.com/?page_id=60

TOOM, ANDRE. "Word problems are very valuable …" excerpted from "Word Problems in Russia and America," academic paper, November 6, 2010; extended version of a talk at the Meeting of the Swedish Mathematical Society, June, 2005. Check out Toom's other articles on math and education, too.
http://www.de.ufpe.br/~toom/travel/sweden05/wp-sweden-new.pdf
http://toomandre.com/my-articles/engeduc/index.htm

—. "For example, coins …" from "Word problems: Applications vs. Mental Manipulatives," *For the Learning of Mathematics*, v. 19 (1), March 1999.
http://toomandre.com/my-articles/engeduc/manipul.pdf

VANHATTUM, SUE. *Playing with Math: Stories from Math Circles, Homeschoolers, and Passionate Teachers*, Delta Stream Media, 2015. VanHattum is a community col-

lege mathematics teacher, math circle leader, and blogger.
http://www.playingwithmath.org

WAY, JENNI. "Learning Mathematics Through Games Series," Nrich Enriching Mathematics website.
http://nrich.maths.org/2489

WHITEHEAD, ALFRED NORTH. "From the very beginning ..." from *The Aims of Education and Other Essays*, Williams & Norgate Limited, 1938.

—. "I will not go so far ..." quoted by W. H. Auden and L. Kronenberger in *The Viking Book of Aphorisms*, Viking Press, 1966.

WHITNEY, HASSLER. "No wonder you hate math ..." quoted by Claudia Zaslavsky in *Fear of Math: How to Get Over It and Get On with Your Life*, Rutgers University Press, 1994.

Index

About the Author

DENISE GASKINS ENJOYS MATH, AND she delights in sharing that joy with young people. "Math is not just rules and rote memory," she says. "Math is like ice cream, with more flavors than you can imagine. And if all you ever do is textbook math, that's like eating broccoli-flavored ice cream."

A veteran homeschooling mother of five, Denise has taught or tutored mathematics at every level from pre-K to undergraduate physics. "Which," she explains, "at least in the recitation class that I taught, was just one story problem after another. What fun!"

Now she writes the popular blog Let's Play Math and manages the Math Teachers at Play monthly math education blog carnival.

A Note from Denise

I hope you enjoyed this book and found some ideas that will help your children enjoy learning.

If you believe this playful approach to math is worth sharing, please consider posting a review at Goodreads.com or at your favorite bookseller's website. Just a few lines would be great. An honest review is the highest compliment you can pay to any author, and your comments help fellow readers discover good books.

Thank you!

—DENISE GASKINS

LETSPLAYMATH@GMAIL.COM

Let's Connect Online

LET'S PLAY MATH BLOG
http://DeniseGaskins.com

FACEBOOK PAGE
http://www.facebook.com/letsplaymath

TWITTER
http://twitter.com/letsplaymath

GOOGLE+
http://plus.google.com/+DeniseGaskins

PINTEREST
http://www.pinterest.com/denisegaskins

EMAIL
LetsPlayMath@gmail.com

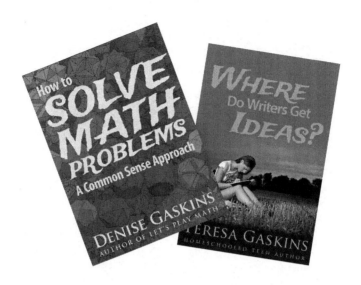

Get Your Free Booklets

Are you looking for playful ways to help your children enjoy math and writing? Visit the website below to claim your free learning guides:

How to Solve a Math Problem: Teach your children to use this four-step, common-sense method to think their way through math stumpers.

Where Do Writers Get Ideas? Inspire your budding writers with tips from homeschooled teen author Teresa Gaskins.

And as a *Tabletop Academy Press Updates* subscriber, you'll be one of the first to hear about new books, revisions, and sales or other promotions.

TabletopAcademy.net/Subscribe

The *Math You Can Play* Series

ARE YOU TIRED OF THE daily homework drama? Do your children sigh, fidget, whine, stare out the window—anything except work on their math? Wouldn't it be wonderful if math was something your kids WANTED to do?

With the *Math You Can Play* series, your kids can practice their math skills by playing games with basic items you already have around the house, such as playing cards and dice.

Math games pump up mental muscle, reduce the fear of failure, and develop a positive attitude toward mathematics. Through playful interaction, games strengthen a child's intuitive understanding of numbers and build problem-solving strategies. Mastering a math game can be hard work, but kids do it willingly because it is fun.

So what are you waiting for? Clear off a table, grab a deck of cards, and let's play some math!

Counting & Number Bonds:
Math Games for Early Learners

Preschool to Second Grade: Young children can play with counting and number recognition, while older students explore place value, build number sense, and begin learning the basics of addition.

Addition & Subtraction:
Math Games for Elementary Students

Kindergarten to Fourth Grade: Children develop mental flexibility by playing with numbers, from basic math facts to the hundreds and beyond. Logic games build strategic thinking skills, and dice games give students hands-on experience with probability.

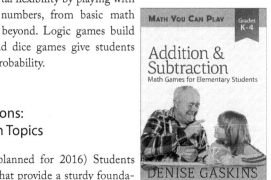

Multiplication & Fractions:
Math Games for Tough Topics

Second to Sixth Grade: (planned for 2016) Students learn several math models that provide a sturdy founda-

268

tion for understanding multiplication and fractions. The games feature times table facts and more advanced concepts such as division, fractions, decimals, and multistep mental math.

Prealgebra & Geometry: Math Games for Middle School

Fourth to Ninth Grade: (planned for 2017) Older students can handle more challenging games that develop logic and problem-solving skills. Here are playful ways to explore positive and negative integers, number properties, mixed operations, functions, and coordinate geometry.

Strategy & Reasoning: Games that Build Thinking Skills

For All Ages: (Planned for 2018.) Strategy games combine a relief from tedious textbook work with the adventure of creatively logical reasoning. Children who play strategy games learn to enjoy the challenge of thinking hard.